Human **Anatomy** AND **Physiology** I & II

Laboratory Manual, **3E**

BIOLOGY FACULTY
OAKTON COMMUNITY COLLEGE

Written by: Bruce D. Wingerd

This lab manual was derived in part from the works of Bruce D. Wingerd. Since 1980, Bruce Wingerd's writings and labs have delivered to students the tools they need to gain a deeper understanding of the human body and reach their full academic potential.

lab | Byte
BRUCE WINGERD

flexible & affordable learning solutions™

Chief Executive Officer: Jon K. Earl

President, College: Lucas Tomasso
President, Private Sector: Dawn Earl
Regional Manager: Greg Bartell

Print Solutions Manager: Connie Dayton
Digital Solutions Manager: Amber Wahl
Developmental & Production Coordinator: Rhiannon Nelson
Senior Project Coordinator: Dan Woods
Senior Project Coordinator: Peggy Li
Project Coordinator: Erica Rieck
Project Coordinator: Jessie Steigauf
Production Assistant: Stephanie Larson

Consulting Editors: Bruce D. Wingerd, M.S.
                     Suzanne S. Frucht, Ph.D.
                     Anna M. Kats, M.S., Florida Atlantic University
                     Michelle F. Cavallo, M.S., Florida Atlantic University
                     John F. Wiginton, Ph.D., University of Mississippi
                     Stephanie R. Dillon, Ph.D., Florida State University

Cover Design: Dan Woods

ISBN-13: 978-1-59984-806-8

Published by bluedoor, LLC
          10949 Bren Road East
          Minneapolis, MN 55343-9613
          800-979-1624
          www.bluedoorpublishing.com

Printed in the United States of America.
10 9 8 7 6 5 4 3 2

TABLE OF CONTENTS

Chapter

OCC BIOLOGY DEPARTMENT SAFETY RULES

The following is a list of required safety rules that will be enforced during the course. These rules have been established for your safety and the safety of your peers and your instructor. If you fail to follow these rules, you will be asked to leave the laboratory which may result in failure for that day's assignment(s).

- Identify and locate exits, fire extinguishers, chemical showers, first aid kit, and eye wash stations. In case of fire, evacuate room, exit the building and assemble outside.
- Wear safety goggles during exercises in which solutions are being mixed and/or heated as directed by instructor.
- Never eat or drink in the laboratory.
- Do not pipette anything by mouth.
- Do not apply cosmetics or lip balm in the laboratory.
- Dress properly for laboratory work:
  - o Long hair should be tied back.
  - o No dangling jewelry.
  - o No baggy clothing
  - o No open-toed shoes.
  - o No shorts.
  - o No skirts above the knee.
- Wear clothing that, if damaged, would not be a serious loss, or use aprons or laboratory coats, since some chemicals may damage fabrics.
- Do not wear contacts during cadaver labs. Contact lenses may trap irritants on the surface of the eyes.
- Keep hands away from face, eyes and mouth when working with chemicals or preserved specimens.
- Wash hands thoroughly with soap and water after handling chemicals or preserved specimens.
- Wear gloves when dissecting or handling preserved specimens or biohazardous materials (blood, urine, saliva, etc.).
- All waste and broken materials should be disposed of as directed by your instructor.
- Keep purses and backpacks out of aisles to avoid people from tripping over handles or straps.
- Report any accident or injury to the laboratory instructor immediately.
- Do not enter laboratory unless your instructor is present.
- If you are pregnant or may be pregnant, please tell your instructor.

I, _____, have read and understand the biology department safety
            (print name)

rules. I understand that if I fail to abide by these rules I may be asked to leave the laboratory which may result in failure for that day's assignment(s).

Signed: _____ Date: _____

OCC A&P LABORATORY GUIDELINES

If any of the guidelines are violated, you will be asked to leave class which may result in failure for the day's assignment(s).

General Safety:

1. No eating or drinking is allowed in the lab room at anytime.

2. Students are not allowed in the lab room unless the instructor is present. Please wait outside the laboratory until your instructor arrives.

Microscopes:

1. You will be assigned a microscope at the start of every laboratory session when microscopes are required. It is your responsibility to clean and maintain this scope during your class period. Please notify your instructor if there are any problems with your microscope.

2. Please make sure to clean the oil objective (100X) and the parts of your microscope that contain oil with lens cleaner after use. Your instructor will demonstrate the proper procedure.

3. Please put your microscope away following the posted instructions on the microscope cabinet door. Also, please put your numbered scope in the same numbered shelf.
   - Condenser should be down.
   - Scanning objective should be in place.
   - Make sure scope is turned off.
   - Wrap electrical cord around eyepieces (not by light source).

4. When using prepared slides, please clean and return them to the appropriate numbered tray after use.

Cadavers:

1. During lab, the cadavers must be kept covered with moist towels at all times. Expose only the section of muscles you are currently viewing. Be very careful with the hands and feet as they dry out quickly. Spray the exposed areas with preservative or water every ten minutes. Check periodically to make sure the towels are moist. When you are done using cadavers replace towels and plastic cover.

2. Please do not pull on muscles, tendons, blood vessels or nerves. They are very fragile and tear easily. Use only probes when examining the cadavers. DO NOT USE DISSECTING NEEDLES, PENS OR PENCILS!

3. Do not uncover the face.

4. Please be respectful.

5. You **may not** take pictures or video footage of the cadavers.

6. Only 3 cadavers may be used at a time.

7. You must purchase your own gloves for dissection. The bookstore sells them.

8. As you work on cadavers, wash gloves as you move from cadaver to cadaver.

Specimens:

1. If you are dissecting cats or any other animal specimens, please remember to bring your dissecting gloves. The prep room will not provide any. No exceptions will be made.

2. Make sure you cover your animal specimens with wet paper towels and then place in a plastic bag to keep it moist. Do not forget to label it with your name or your group name. Your instructor will show you where to store them.

3. If you use wax trays, please make sure you wash with soap and water and then pat them dry with paper towel. This prevents contamination. Reline wax trays with new paper towel.

4. Please do not dispose of any solids, cat hair, or skin or any other parts of specimens in the lab sinks.

5. You must purchase your own gloves for dissection. The bookstore sells them.

Models:

1. Models are available for viewing during class time or during tutorial time. The Biology Prep Room does not give models for viewing outside lab or tutor time. Instructional Support Services may have some models available for private viewing during their business hours.

2. There are model key notebook binders in your lab room to use during lab time or tutoring for some of the models. These binders will help you name structures on the models. You are welcome to make copies if you choose to do so.

3. Please do not use pens, pencils, markers, etc. to point to models. Please use pipe cleaners provided.

4. When you are finished using a model reassemble before putting away.

Bone Boxes:

1. Do not use pens, pencils, markers, etc to identify structures on bones. Use the pipecleaners provided.

2. Real bones are extremely fragile and expensive to replace, be very careful.

3. When using bone boxes, keep bones with their respective boxes and places in boxes. Do not mix bones with other bone boxes.

The study of human anatomy is an important component to any course in anatomy and physiology. This chapter introduces you to basic anatomy. It provides an overview of anatomical terminology and the organization of the human body.

The laboratory exercises in this unit correlate to Chapter 1 in your textbook and to the following BIO 231 course objective:

1. Utilize the appropriate relational anatomic terms as they apply to position, plane and location.

THE LANGUAGE OF ANATOMY

Anatomy is the study of body structure. It uses a universal terminology to describe the location and appearance of body parts, enabling health workers around the world to speak in a common language. The universal terms are mainly derived from Latin and Greek word parts, which become assembled like a puzzle to form new words. For example, the word cardiovascular is made up of the word parts cardio (heart), vas (vessel), -ul (small), and -ar (pertaining to). When the word parts are combined to form the term cardiovascular, the literal meaning becomes "pertaining to small vessels and the heart."

Many terms in anatomy are composed of three types of word parts. The root is the main word part, carrying the primary meaning of the word. In the term pregastric, the root is gastr-, which means "stomach." The prefix precedes the root and often alters its meaning. In pregastric, the prefix is pre-, which means "before." The suffix follows the root to alter the meaning. In pregastric, the suffix is -ic, which means "pertaining to." Taken as a whole term, pregastric means "pertaining to before the stomach." A sampling of the most common word parts used to form anatomy and medical terms is provided in **Table 1.1**. Understanding the common word parts and how words are constructed often helps you to learn the meanings of the new words.

Table 1.1: Common Word Parts of Anatomy.

Prefixes = Precedes the Root	Word Roots	Suffixes = Follows the Root
a- = without	abdomin = abdomen	-ad = toward
ad- = toward	arterio = artery	-al = pertaining to
dys- = bad, abnormal	cardio = heart	-gen, -genic = formation, produce
hyper- = excessive	dors = back	-itis = inflammation
hypo- = under, below normal	gastro = stomach	-logy = study
inter- = between	hemo = blood	-oid = resemblance to
intra- = within	latero = side	-ous = pertaining to
poly- = many	medio = middle	-oma = abnormal swelling
pre- = before	osteo = bone	-pathy = disease
sub- = beneath	vas = vessel	-scopy = process of viewing

ANATOMICAL POSITION

When using the language of anatomy, an important point of reference that is in common usage is the **anatomical position.** The **anatomical position** is defined as the body in an erect stance, facing forward. The arms are straight, palms forward, and fingers pointing downward at a slight angle. The legs are straight or slightly apart, with the toes pointing forward and flat. A Figure in this position is illustrated in **Figure 1.1**.

Exercise 1.1 Anatomical Position

1. Assume the anatomical position, and have your lab partner share with you the definition to make sure you represent the correct position.

BODY REGIONS

The **body regions** are areas of the body that are identified during a physical examination. They are listed and described in **Table 1.2**. Notice that the body regions in this list are formed from two word parts, a root and a suffix. What do you think is the meaning of the root within the anatomy term "cephalic?"

Table 1.2: Regions of the Body.

Primary Body Regions	Subdivisions

Cephalic: pertaining to the head	**Facial: pertaining to the face**
	   Buccal: pertaining to the cheek
	   Orbital: pertaining to the eye socket
	   Oral: pertaining to the mouth
	   Otic: pertaining to the ear
	   Mental: pertaining to the chin
	   Nasal: pertaining to the nose
	Cranial: pertaining to the cranium
	   Frontal: pertaining to the forehead
	   Occipital: Pertaining to the posterior aspect of head or skull

Cervical: pertaining to the neck	

Trunk	**Thoracic: pertaining to the chest (thorax)**
	   Sternal: pertaining to the breastbone
	   Pectoral (mammary): pertaining to the breast
	Abdominal: pertaining to the anterior trunk below the ribs (abdomen)
	   Umbilical: pertaining to the navel
	Coxal: pertaining to the hip
	Pelvic: pertaining to the pelvis
	   Pelvic: lower anterior pelvis
	   Inguinal: pertaining to the groin
	   Gluteal: pertaining to the buttocks
	   Perineal: pertaining to the region between the anus and external genitalia
	Back (dorsum): the posterior side of the trunk
	   Scapular: pertaining to the shoulder blade
	   Vertebral: pertaining to the spinal column
	   Lumbar: pertaining to the lower back between the ribs and hips (loin)

Upper Limb	**Acromial: Pertaining to the shoulder**
	Axillary: Pertaining to the armpit
	Brachial: Pertaining to the arm
	   Antebrachial: pertaining to the forearm
	   Antecubital: pertaining to the anterior elbow
	   Carpal: pertaining to the wrist
	Manus: pertaining to the hand
	   Palmar: pertaining to the palm of the hand
	   Digital: pertaining to the fingers
	   Pollex: pertaining to the thumb

Lower Limb	**Gluteal: pertaining to the buttock**
	Femoral: pertaining to the thigh
	Patellar: pertaining to the anterior knee
	Popliteal: pertaining to the posterior knee
	Crural: pertaining to the leg
	Sural: pertaining to the posterior leg (calf)
	Fibular (peroneal): pertaining to the side of leg
	Tarsal: pertaining to the ankle
	Pedal: pertaining to the foot
	   Calcaneal: pertaining to the heel
	   Plantar: pertaining to the sole
	   Digital: pertaining to the toes
	   Hallux: pertaining to the big toe

Exercise 1.2 Body Regions

Using yourself and a model or chart in your lab, review the body region terms and their locations.

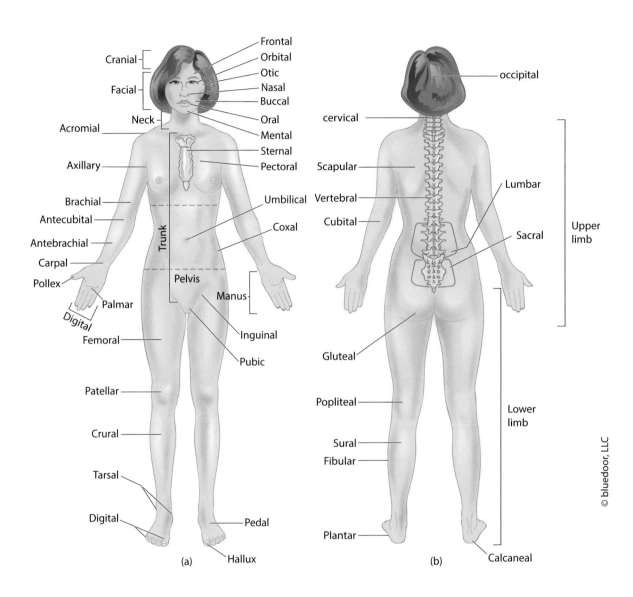

Figure 1.1: The anatomical position. (a) Anterior. (b) Posterior.

© bluedoor, LLC

DIRECTIONAL TERMS

A group of anatomical terms are used to describe the location of body parts. Known as directional terms, they are helpful because they abbreviate otherwise lengthy descriptions of where a body part is located relative to other parts. They use the anatomical position as a point of reference, and are listed in **Table 1.3**. Note that the terms have opposing meanings, such as superior and inferior. Also, when using directional terms you should include a point of reference. For example, to describe the location of the nose you would say "the nose is superior to the chin," rather than "the nose is superior."

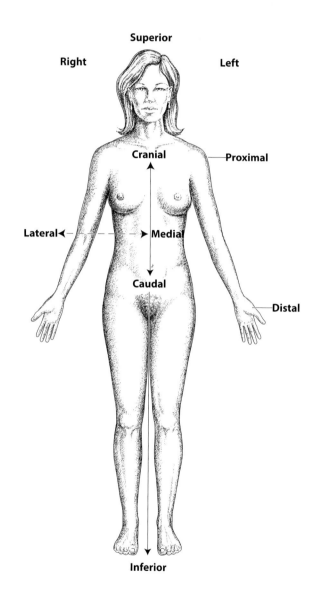

Figure 1.2: Directional terms.

Table 1.3: Directional Terms

Term	Definition	Example
Superior (cranial)	Above. Refers to relative placement between two structures along the long axis of the body.	The heart is superior to the pelvis.
Inferior (caudal)	Below. Refers to relative placement along the long axis of the body.	The chest is inferior to the head.
Anterior (ventral)	Front. Toward the front or belly side.	The nose is on the anterior side of the head.
Posterior (dorsal)	Back. Toward the back.	The spinal cord extends down the posterior side of the body.
Medial	Toward the midline, which is an imaginary line that extends vertically down the middle.	The sternum (breastbone) is medial to the ribs.
Lateral	Away from the midline.	The ears are lateral to the nose.
Superficial (external)	Toward the surface of the body.	The skin is superficial to visceral organs.
Deep (internal)	Away from the surface of the body.	The heart lies deep to the sternum.
Proximal	Nearer the trunk. Toward a structure's origin or point of attachment to the trunk.	The shoulder is proximal to the elbow.
Distal	Farther from the trunk. Away from a structure's origin or point of attachment to the trunk.	The wrist is distal to the shoulder.
*Note: Anatomical terminology is slightly different when applied to four-legged animals. The following terminology is applied to humans and four-legged animals:		
In humans, the following terms are interchangeable.		
Cranial and superior Caudal and inferior ventral and anterior dorsal and posterior		
In four-legged animals, the following terms are interchangeable:		
Cranial and anterior Caudal and posterior Ventral and inferior Dorsal and superior		

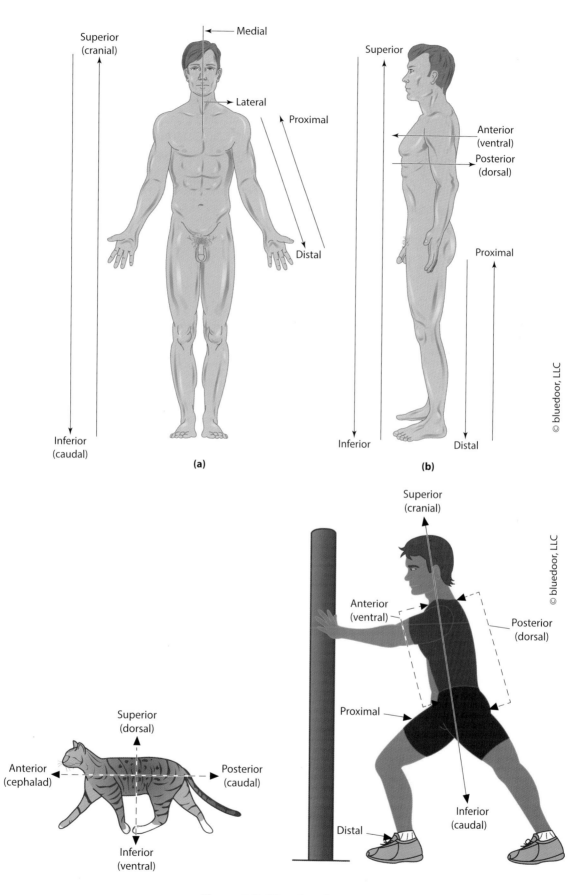

© bluedoor, LLC

© bluedoor, LLC

Figure 1.3: Directional terms.

PLANES AND SECTIONS

A **plane** is an imaginary flat surface. It is useful in anatomy because it can describe how a slice, or section, can extend through the body. Three major planes are used in anatomy: frontal plane, sagittal plane, and transverse plane. The frontal plane extends through the long axis of the body (that is, along the body's length), dividing the body into anterior (front) and posterior (back) portions. The sagittal plane also extends through the body's long axis, but it divides the body into right and left portions. A sagittal plane dividing the body into equal right and left halves is called midsagittal, whereas one that divides unequally is called parasagittal. The transverse plane extends perpendicular to the frontal and sagittal planes to divide the body into superior (upper) and inferior (lower) portions. A section made along the transverse plane is often referred to as a cross section.

On microscopic slides, the abbreviation for a longitudinal section (sagittal or frontal) is l.s. Cross sections are abbreviated x.s. or c.s.

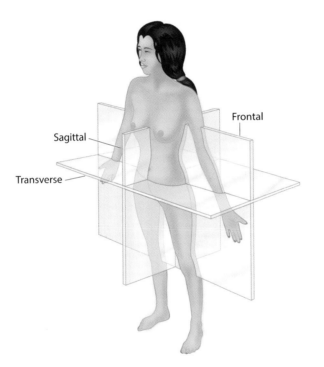

Figure 1.4: Planes and sections.

Exercise 1.3: Planes and Sections

1. Review the planes and sections that are frequently used in human anatomy.

2. Using pig kidneys, work with a partner to demonstrate planes and sections by cutting through the kidney with a knife. Make a section through the frontal plane, then the sagittal plane and finally the transverse plane. Draw the appearance of the kidney after each section is made.

Sketch of kidney after the frontal section:

Sketch of the kidney after the sagittal section:

Sketch of the kidney after the transverse section:

3. If a cardboard tube is available in your lab, work with a partner to cut through the tube as if it were a tubular structure in the body (e.g. blood vessel, small intestine, etc.). Make a section through the frontal plane first, then the sagittal plane, and finally the transverse plane and sketch the appearance of the tube after each slice.

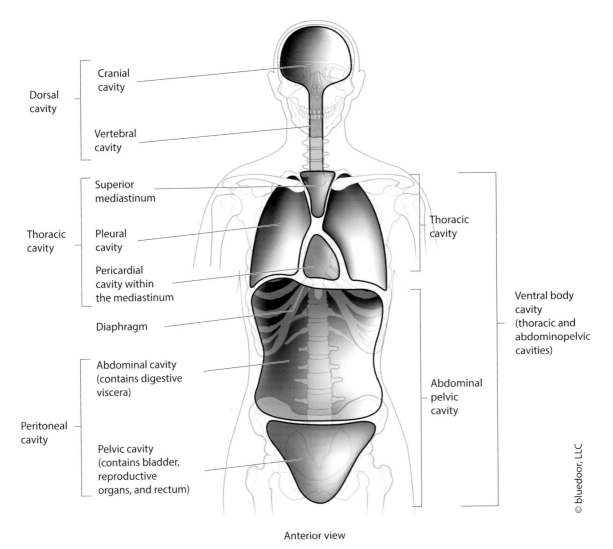

Anterior view

Figure 1.5: Body cavities.

BODY CAVITIES AND SEROUS MEMBRANES

A **body cavity** is a space that is lined with a membrane. Body cavities are never empty; they are filled with organs and their supporting structures (blood vessels, nerves, fibrous tissues, and fluids). There are two main cavities in the human body; dorsal and ventral (**Figure 1.5**). The **dorsal cavity** is located within the posterior (dorsal) side of the body, and includes the cranial cavity containing the brain, and the **vertebral cavity** that houses the spinal cord.

The **ventral cavity** includes the spaces on the ventral side of the body, such as the thoracic cavity and abdominopelvic cavity. The **thoracic cavity** fills the chest region, and contains the heart, lungs, and major vessels of the heart. It includes several smaller cavities: the **pericardial cavity**, which contains the heart, and two **pleural cavities**, each of which contain a lung. In addition, the area superior to the heart is called the mediastinum, which contains the major blood vessels and the thymus gland. The thoracic cavity is separated from the abdominopelvic cavity by the muscular diaphragm. The **abdominopelvic cavity** is the large area below the diaphragm, divided into the superior abdominal cavity and the inferior pelvic cavity, the peritoneal cavity, as the terms, pericardial and pleural cavities, are mentioned on page 10. The **abdominal cavity** houses the stomach, liver, gallbladder, pancreas, small intestine, kidneys, and part of the large intestine. The **pelvic cavity** contains the reproductive organs, the urinary bladder, and part of the large intestine.

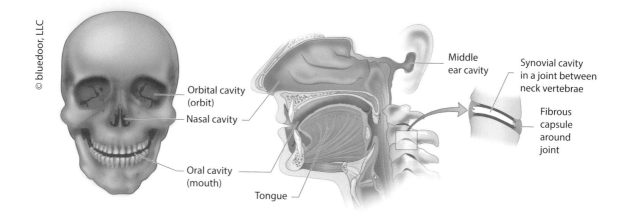

© bluedoor, LLC

Orbital cavity (orbit)

Nasal cavity

Oral cavity (mouth)

Tongue

Middle ear cavity

Synovial cavity in a joint between neck vertebrae

Fibrous capsule around joint

Figure 1.6: Other Body Cavities.

Other body cavities include the **oral cavity, nasal cavity, orbital cavities, middle ear cavities**, and **synovial cavities**. The first four cavities are located in the head and open to the exterior of the body. Synovial cavities are found in freely moveable joints such as your knee, hip, vertebrae.

Membranes are thin sheets of cells and proteins that line all of the openings and cavities of the body. There are several types of membranes in the body; we will study each type in Chapter 4. For now, let's examine one type, called serous membranes. **Serous membranes** line the inside walls of the ventral cavities. They also cover most of the visceral, or internal, organs of the ventral cavities. Each serous membrane consists of an outer layer that attaches to the cavity wall, called a parietal layer, and an inner layer that adheres to an inner organ, called a visceral layer. A small space separates the two layers, and a small amount of serous fluid is produced by the cells in the membrane to reduce friction between the two layers when organs shift in position.

The **serous membrane** compartmentalizes the organs. The serous membranes are named for the organs and cavities with which they are associated. The serous membrane associated with the heart is the **pericardium**, the membrane associated with the lungs is the **pleura**, and the membrane associated with the abdominal organs is the **peritoneum**. Each of these membranes includes a **parietal layer** and a **visceral layer**, separated by a small cavity. Serous membranes prevent infection from spreading from one organ to another in the ventral body cavities.

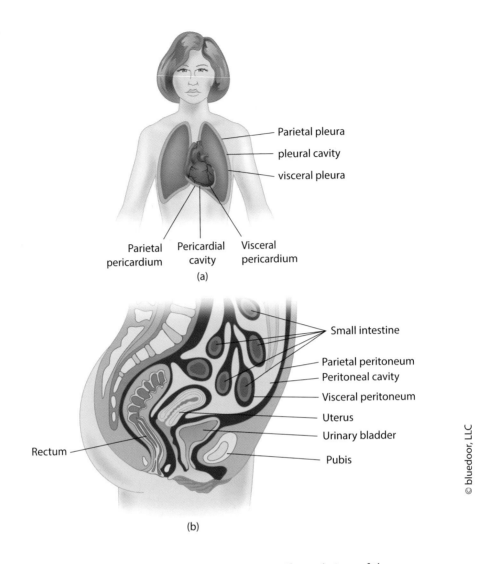

Parietal pleura
pleural cavity
visceral pleura

Parietal   Pericardial   Visceral
pericardium   cavity   pericardium

(a)

Small intestine
Parietal peritoneum
Peritoneal cavity
Visceral peritoneum
Uterus
Urinary bladder
Rectum
Pubis

© bluedoor, LLC

(b)

Figure 1.7: Serous membranes. (a) Coronal view/frontal view of thorax.
(b) Mid-sagittal view of the abdominopelvic cavity.

Exercise 1.4: Body Cavities and Serous Membranes

1. Review the body cavities and serous membranes of the body, using illustrations and models.

ABDOMINOPELVIC DIVISIONS

The **abdominopelvic cavity** is divided into smaller portions to aid in the description of various organs. Two alternate "maps" have been established. One scheme divides the cavity into nine abdominopelvic regions. Creating what looks like a "tic tac toe" grid, two vertical and two horizontal lines are drawn. The vertical lines begin medial to each nipple and extend from the diaphragm to the pelvic area. The upper horizontal line extends across the abdomen just inferior to the lower ribs and stomach, and the lower horizontal line just inferior to the top of the hip bones. The nine regions that result are, from top right to lower left, right hypochondriac, epigastric, left hypochondriac, right lumbar, umbilical, left lumbar, right inguinal, hypogastric, and left inguinal.

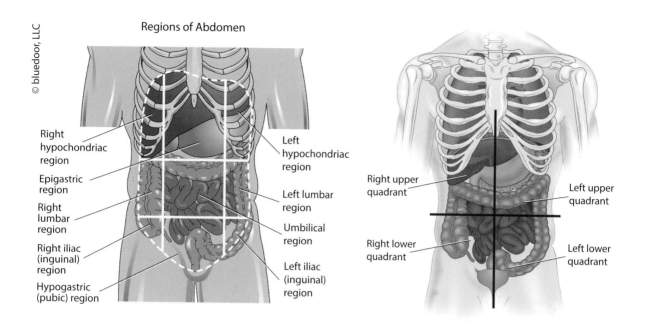

Regions of Abdomen

Right hypochondriac region

Epigastric region

Right lumbar region

Right iliac (inguinal) region

Hypogastric (pubic) region

Left hypochondriac region

Left lumbar region

Umbilical region

Left iliac (inguinal) region

Right upper quadrant

Left upper quadrant

Right lower quadrant

Left lower quadrant

Figure 1.8: (a) Abdominopelvic regions. (b) The four quadrants.

The second scheme dividing the abdominopelvic cavity creates four regions, or quadrants, and is in common clinical use. Formed by one vertical line and one horizontal line that meet at the umbilicus (navel), they are called the right upper quadrant (RUQ), the left upper quadrant (LUQ), the right lower quadrant (RLQ), and the left lower quadrant (LLQ).

Exercise 1.5: Abdominopelvic Divisions

1. Review the abdominopelvic regions described in the previous paragraph by using **Figure 1.8** and models.

ORGANS AND SYSTEMS

In order to become familiar with the body's organizational plan, an overview of the body's organs and systems is an important step. An **organ** is a structure with a defined shape that is composed of more than one type of tissue, and performs a particular role in the body. Organs include the brain, heart, stomach, and urinary bladder. Organs are combined to form a larger group called a **system**, which performs a more general role to support health. There are eleven systems of the body, which are described with their organs in **Table 1.4**. Together, the systems seek to maintain homeostasis, which is the physiological state of equilibrium, in an effort to achieve survival.

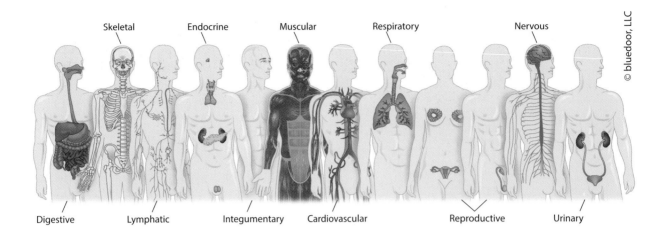

Skeletal   Endocrine   Muscular   Respiratory   Nervous

Digestive   Lymphatic   Integumentary   Cardiovascular   Reproductive   Urinary

© bluedoor, LLC

Figure 1.9: The eleven systems.

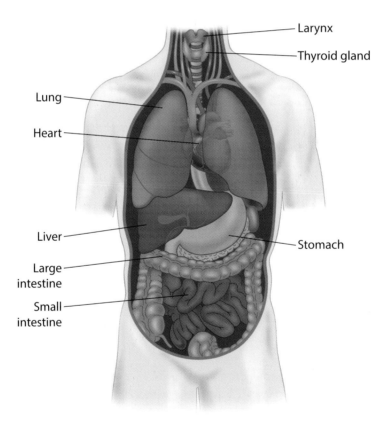

Larynx

Thyroid gland

Lung

Heart

Liver

Stomach

Large intestine

Small intestine

© bluedoor, LLC

Figure 1.10: Major visceral organs.

Exercise 1.6: Organs and Systems

1. Using a torso model in the lab, identify the organs and systems described in **Table 1.4**.

Table 1.4: The Eleven Systems and Their Organs

Organ System	Major Component Organs	Function
Integumentary	Skin Cutaneous sense organs Glands	Protects underlying structures, prevention of fluid loss, temperature regulation Excretes salts and urea Produces vitamin D
Skeletal	Bones, joints Tendons Ligaments	Supports and protects softer body parts, stores minerals, produces blood cells Provides levers for muscle action
Muscular	Skeletal muscles	Provides body movement, produces heat
Nervous	Brain, spinal cord, nerves, sensory receptors	Monitors changes in the environment, interprets the changes, and initiates responses
Endocrine	Pituitary gland, thyroid gland, parathyroid glands, adrenal glands, pancreas, gonads	Alters the activities of cells by the release of hormones in an effort to respond to changes in the body
Cardiovascular	Heart, blood vessels, blood	Transports blood, hormones, and ions throughout all areas of the body Delivers oxygen and glucose to cells Removes carbon dioxide and other wastes
Lymphatic/Immunity	Spleen, thymus, tonsils, lymph nodes, lymphoid vessels	Protects body from foreign particles and cells, removes dead and diseased cells, recycles fluid back into cardiovascular system
Respiratory	Nasal cavities, pharynx, larynx, trachea, bronchi, lungs	Gas exchange between the bloodstream and the external environment Contributes to the acid-base balance of the blood
Digestive	Mouth, salivary glands, pharynx, esophagus, stomach, small intestine, pancreas, liver, large intestine, gallbladder	Simplifies food particles into their basic components to enable their absorption into the bloodstream Removes undigested residue from the body as feces
Urinary	Kidneys, ureters, urinary bladder, urethra	Forms urine in order to maintain water balance, salt balance, pH, and nitrogenous waste levels in the blood Maintains water, electrolyte and acid-base balance of the blood
Reproductive	Male: testes, ductus deferens, urethra, penis, scrotum Female: ovaries, uterine tubes, uterus, vagina	Provides gametes for fertilization in order to create new individuals Female uterus houses developing fetus. Mammary glands provide nourishment for infant

CHAPTER 1 REVIEW

Name _____

Instructor _____

1. Which of the following is an incorrect part of the anatomical position?
   a. face forward
   b. body erect and upright
   c. palms turned to the posterior
   d. toes pointing forward

2. Which of the following regions is part of the thorax?
   a. crural
   b. popliteal
   c. sternal
   d. inguinal

3. The abdominal region includes the
   a. acromial
   b. umbilical
   c. brachial
   d. femoral

4. Within which of the following abdominopelvic regions would you find the stomach?
   a. epigastric region
   b. right hypochondriac region
   c. umbilical region
   d. left inguinal region

5. The pancreas is part of the _____ system and is located within the _____ cavity.
   a. urinary; abdominal
   b. digestive; pelvic
   c. digestive; abdominal
   d. respiratory; thoracic

LANGUAGE OF ANATOMY

Use the word parts in **Table 1.1** to form anatomy terms from the meanings provided.

6. study of the heart: Example: cardiology

7. pertaining to the back: _____

8. forming from the heart: _____

9. abnormal swelling of the stomach: _____

10. pertaining to beneath the abdomen: _____

11. preceding bone disease: _____

12. pertaining to the middle: _____

ANATOMICAL POSITION AND BODY REGIONS

A. Label **Figure 1.11** with the correct body regions from the terms presented in **Table 1.2**:

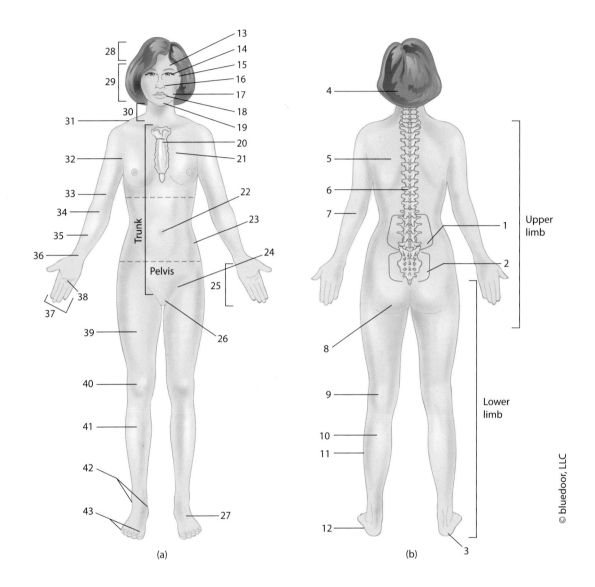

Figure 1.11: The anatomical position. (a) Anterior. (b) Posterior.

© bluedoor, LLC

DIRECTIONAL TERMS

B. Using **Table 1.3**, fill in the spaces with the correct terms:

1. The head is _____ to the thorax.

2. Your ears are _____ to your nose.

3. The abdomen is _____ to the neck.

4. The right elbow is _____ to the right wrist.

5. The skin is _____ to the muscles of the body.

6. The muscles of the chest are _____ to the muscles of the back.

C. Identify the directional terms on **Figure 1.12**.

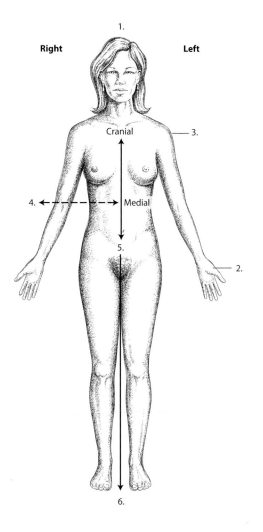

Figure 1.12: Dirctional terms.

D. Review the planes and sections that are frequently used in human anatomy and complete the labels on **Figure 1.13**.

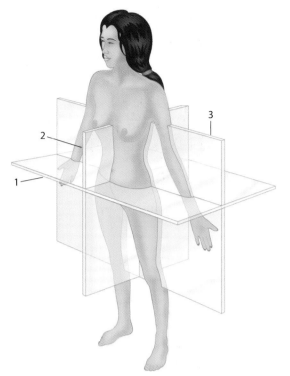

Figure 1.13: Planes and sections.

E. Complete the labels on the diagram (**Figure 1.14a**).

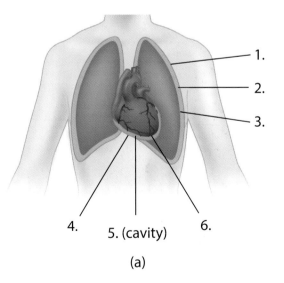

1.
2.
3.
4.
5. (cavity)
6.

(a)

Figure 1.14a: Serous membranes. (a) Frontal/coronal view of thorax.

F. Complete the labels on the diagram (**Figure 1.14b**).

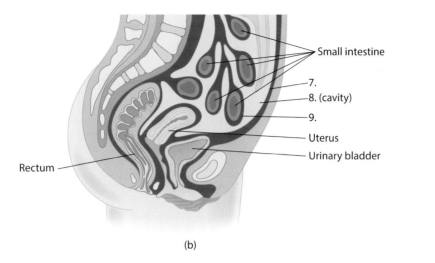

Small intestine

7.

8. (cavity)

9.

Uterus

Urinary bladder

Rectum

(b)

Figure 1.14b: Serous membranes. (b) Mid-sagittal view of abdominopelvic cavity.

© bluedoor, LLC

G. Draw the vertical and horizontal lines onto **Figure 1.15** to establish the nine abdominopelvic regions, and label them.

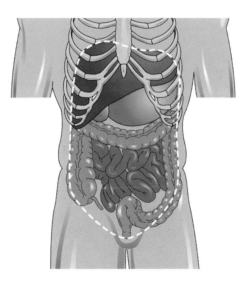

Figure 1.15: Abdominopelvic regions.

© bluedoor, LLC

H. Using the information provided in **Table 1.4**, complete the labels in **Figure 1.16** by filling in the blanks with the correct systems.

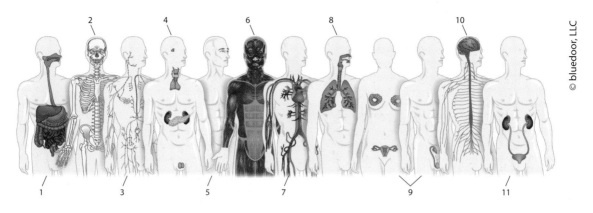

Figure 1.16: The eleven systems.

© bluedoor, LLC

I. Complete the labels in **Figure 1.17** by filling the blanks with the correct organs, which are listed within **Table 1.4**.

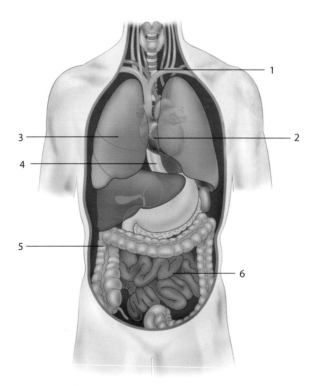

Figure 1.17: Major visceral organs.

© bluedoor, LLC

THE MICROSCOPE AND CELLS

Laboratory Objectives

The theme of Chapter 2 is the microscopic world. You will learn how to use the key instrument for studying this world, the compound microscope, and apply it in a series of exercises that will teach you about cell structure and function.

The laboratory exercises in this unit correlate to Chapters 2 and 3 in your textbook and to the following BIO 231 course objectives:

1. Examine basic chemistry of biologically important molecules and reactions.
2. Differentiate between organelles within human cells.

THE MICROSCOPE

The microscope has made it possible to study structures too small to be seen with the unaided eye. It is an instrument that magnifies an image, enabling very small objects to be observed. In addition to magnification, a microscope also provides visual clarity, or **resolution**, to enable tiny objects to be studied. Resolution refers to the ability to distinguish between two objects; the greater the resolution, the smaller the distance between them. Without a microscope, a normal human eye has a resolution of about 0.2 mm, which means that the eye can distinguish between two objects that are no less than 0.2 mm apart. The light microscopes that you will use in the lab have a resolution of about a thousand times that, or 0.2 μm. As you will see, they can magnify an image up to 1,000 times.

The following exercises will give you an opportunity to explore one of the greatest tools of science, the microscope. They will show you its proper handling and use in preparation for microscopic studies that you will encounter throughout the course. But first, you must learn how to handle and care for the microscope.

© 2015 bluedoor, LLC

Exercise 2.1: Handling and Care of the Microscope

Study the following list when preparing to use a microscope:

1. Carry a microscope by supporting it in both hands in an upright position. One hand should grasp the microscope arm, while the other provides a flat platform for its base. Place it down on a flat surface that has been cleared of debris.

2. If your microscope has a rheostat, which adjusts light intensity, make sure it is turned to minimum light intensity before turning on the light.

3. Clean all lenses by wiping with grit-free lens paper. Never use a paper towel or any other material to clean the lens to avoid making permanent scratches.

4. When you adjust focus, always begin with the lowest power first. Avoid contacting the lens to the microscope slide on the stage.

5. If your microscope is not working as you expect, notify your lab instructor immediately. Do not attempt to make repairs by removing or adjusting parts.

ANATOMY OF THE COMPOUND MICROSCOPE

There are many types of microscopes. Compound microscopes, stereomicroscopes, and electron microscopes are the three most common types. In the following exercise, you will learn the parts of the microscope most commonly used in labs around the world: the compound microscope.

The compound microscope that you will use is composed of numerous parts, many of which are adjustable to enable you to change magnification and resolution power. The parts are shown in **Figure 3.1**, and include the following:

- **Base:** The supportive bottom piece of the microscope. The base includes the following part:

    Substage light: A light within the base providing the light source for illumination of the specimen. A switch, usually at the side or front of the base, turns it on and off, and a dial (rheostat) adjusts the light intensity. In some microscopes, the substage light is replaced by a mirror, which requires an external light source.

- **Head:** Also called the body tube, it is the upper part that contains the viewing pieces (the lenses and rotating nosepiece). The head includes:

    Ocular lenses: The eyepieces, which are two removable lenses that you look through to observe the microscope specimen. Some microscopes have a single ocular lens. Most ocular lenses have a magnification of 10X, increasing the observed size of the specimen by a factor of 10. Some ocular lenses have a pointer, which is a dark line on the glass lens. It enables the viewer to point to a part of the specimen.

    Nosepiece: Located below the ocular lenses, it serves as an attachment for the objective lenses. The viewer can rotate the nosepiece to change from one objective lens to another.

    Objective lenses: Three or four objective lenses that are usually attached to the nosepiece, each with a different magnification: usually 4X, or scanning; 10X, or low power; 40X, or high power; and if present, 100X, or oil immersion. The magnification levels are written on each objective lens.

- **Arm:** The narrow, vertical part connecting the head and base. It may be straight or curved. The microscope arm contains the following parts:

Stage: The flat platform connected to the arm and suspended beneath the objective lenses, upon which the microscope slide with its specimen is placed. The stage often includes either a *mechanical stage* or *stage clips*, both of which keep the slide stationary during viewing.

Coarse adjustment knobs: Two knobs on either side of the base of the arm. They are usually the largest knobs on the arm. Turning them raises and lowers the stage, bringing it closer to or further from the objective lens. Thus, these knobs control the focus. You may use either knob or both for the same effect. The coarse adjustment knob should only be used at scanning power (4X) or low power (10X) to avoid contacting the objective lens with the microscope slide.

Fine adjustment knobs: Two knobs usually located in the center of each coarse adjustment knob. The knob on either side is used for precision focusing, since they raise or lower the stage at very small increments.

Condenser: A lens located just below the stage, it concentrates light on the specimen. In many microscopes, the condenser includes a knob that raises and lowers it to control light intensity. For exercises in this manual, the best position for the condenser is close to the stage.

Iris diaphragm lever: A lever located beneath the condenser, it opens and closes the iris diaphragm attached to it. The iris diaphragm regulates light passing through the condenser.

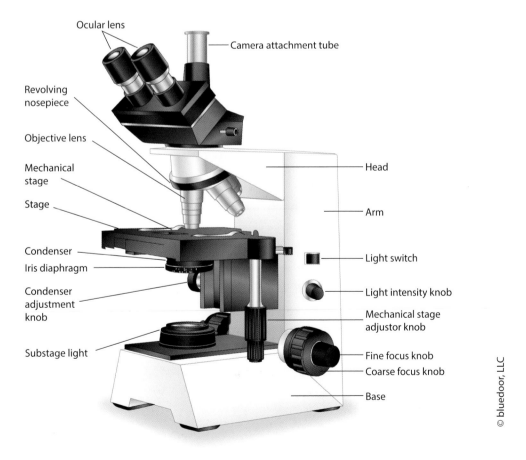

Figure 2.1: The parts of a compound microscope.

Exercise 2.2: Determining Magnification

The total magnification (TM) of a specimen being viewed with a microscope is determined by multiplying the ocular lens power and the objective lens power. For example, using an ocular lens (10X) and the high power objective lens (40X) will provide 400X total magnification. Fill in the blanks to complete the sentences and equations:

1. If you adjust the objective lens to low power (10X), the TM is reduced to _____.

2. Using the oil immersion lens, the TM becomes _____.

3. Scanning a specimen is performed with a TM that equals _____.

USING THE COMPOUND MICROSCOPE

Now that you are familiar with the microscope, it is important to experience how to actually use it. The following exercise offers this opportunity, providing you with a checklist that you should refer to whenever you are asked to perform a microscopic observation.

Exercise 2.3: Using the Compound Microscope

Carefully remove your assigned microscope from the lab cabinet and carry it to your work area; carry it as instructed at the beginning of this chapter! Follow this list, and repeat the steps whenever you use the microscope in the future:

1. Unwind the cord and plug it in.

2. Clean the ocular, objective, and condenser lenses with lens paper (only), provided by your lab instructor.

3. Turn the light intensity knob down and turn on the substage light, then turn up the light intensity slowly until the light appears. If the light does not turn on, push the red button near the switch to reset the breaker. If the light still fails to appear, contact your lab instructor to replace the light bulb.

4. Adjust the nosepiece to lock in the scanning objective lens over the light aperture (the small opening) on the stage; you will feel it shift slightly when it is in place.

5. Obtain a prepared microscope slide with the letter "E" from your instructor. Place it on the stage and secure it with stage clamps or stage clips to prevent movement. If your microscope has a mechanical stage, practice moving it into its various positions.

6. Orient the "E" on the slide with the location of the scanning objective lens by using the mechanical stage (if your microscope does not have a mechanical stage, you will have to move the slide position with your fingers).

7. Check the location of the condenser; adjust its location to as close to the stage as possible, if it is not in this position already.

8. If your microscope stage is moveable, use the coarse adjustment knob to raise the stage as far up as it allows. If your stage is not moveable, move the nosepiece downward until the objective lens is as close to the slide and stage as possible. In either case, the microscope mechanism will stop before contact is made between the objective lens and the slide.

9. If your microscope has two ocular lenses (called a binocular microscope), adjust the distance between the two lenses until it is comfortable for your eyes.

10. Now you are ready to look through the ocular lens (or lenses). As you do so, adjust the focus with the coarse adjustment knob to focus on the "E". Compared to normal vision, what is different about the "E" under the microscope? _____

11. With the "E" in focus, move the slide around using the mechanical stage (or if necessary, with your fingers). What do you notice is different about the "E" when moving it?

12. Move the "E" back into the center of the field of view. Change your objective lens to low power, and observe it through the microscope. If adjusted properly, changing objective lenses should not change the focus on the specimen. This feature is called parfocal.

13. Now, use the fine adjustment knob to sharpen the focus. Although most microscopes are *parfocal*, fine adjustment will usually be necessary to improve resolution of the image.

14. Use the iris diaphragm lever to change the amount of light falling on the image. By doing so, you are able to change the *contrast* of the image, which can improve resolution of certain types of samples.

15. Change your objective lens to high power, and observe the letter "E". To improve resolution, focus with the fine adjustment knob ONLY.

16. Most anatomy and physiology lab uses of the microscope do not use the oil immersion lens. Although it improves magnification, the oil may damage the lens, so it is not recommended unless deemed essential by your instructor. If you use it, your instructor will provide an oil dropper. Apply a single drop of oil to the part of the slide you wish to observe. Then move the objective lens from high power to oil immersion, and focus with the fine adjustment knob (only).

DEPTH PERCEPTION

Depth perception is the ability to distinguish objects at varying depths in a specimen. It is affected by the amount of light coming through the iris diaphragm. As the light is reduced, the contrast increases.

Exercise 2.4: Perceiving Depth

1. Obtain a slide with colored crossed threads and focus it under low magnification and locate the point where the three threads cross each other.

2. Decrease the amount of light coming through the diaphragm.

3. With the coarse adjustment, focus down until the threads are out of focus.

4. Then slowly focus up again, identifying which thread comes into focus first, second, and third.

5. Observe the stage and determine if it falls or rises as you move the course adjustment away from you (forward). If the stage rises, the first clearly focused thread is the top one.

6. Identify which colored thread was the top, middle, and bottom.

   a. Top thread _____

   b. Middle thread _____

   c. Bottom thread _____

Observing a Tissue Slide

1. Now that you are more familiar with the parts of the microscope and its respective functions, obtain a tissue slide from your instructor. Following the same steps you used to observe the 'E' slide, observe the tissue slide.

2. Once you focus the tissue at 40X, ask your instructor to view the slide.

3. As you brought the tissue slide into focus and increased magnification from 4X to 40X, what similarities and differences did you note between focusing and magnifying a tissue as compared to the 'E' slide or the crossed threads slide? _____

   _____

4. After you are finished with your microscope observations, always clean up properly:

   • Return slides to appropriate slide tray.

   • Turn off the substage light.

   • Unplug the microscope.

   • If you used oil immersion, clean the slide and objectives with lens paper.

   • Remove the microscope slide and return it to its slide tray.

   • Wrap the electrical cord around the eyepieces.

   • Lower the stage and condenser.

   • Return objective to scanning objective, 4X.

   • **Before you return microscope to the cabinet, let your instructor view your scope.**

CELL STRUCTURE

Cells are the most basic living unit of the human body. Although your body contains roughly 30 trillion cells, they share a common architecture: each is a membrane-enclosed sac containing smaller subunits that provide most of the functions. The structure of a typical cell is divided into three major parts: the **plasma** (or cell) **membrane**, which envelops the rest of the cell; the **cytoplasm**, which consists of functional subunits called **organelles** within a liquid medium known as the **cytosol**; and a prominent structure that contains DNA, the **nucleus**. (These cell parts and their components are discussed in your textbook and are shown in **Figure 2.2**.)

Exercise 2.5: Cell Structure

1. Which organelle may be shaped like a sausage, includes an inner folded membrane, and performs important roles in cellular respiration? _____

2. Which organelle contains ribosomes and serves as the site of protein synthesis? _____

   _____

3. What are the openings in the nuclear membrane called? _____

4. The cytoplasm includes a liquid medium, called the _____.

5. The organelle that appears like a stack of pancakes and prepares materials for exocytosis is the

   _____.

6. The spherical structures in the cytoplasm that contain digesting enzymes are known as

   _____.

7. The outermost layer of the adrenal gland is called the cortex. The cortex is responsible for synthesizing and secreting steroid hormones, such as cortisol. Predict which organelle, smooth ER or rough ER, would be more developed in cells of the adrenal cortex. Explain your reasoning.

   _____

   _____

   _____

8. Predict in which tissue(s) you would expect to find more mitochondria, cardiac muscle or dense regular connective tissue. Explain your reasoning. _____

   _____

   _____

   _____

9. Predict the consequences to tissues if lysosomes were removed from cells. Explain your reasoning. _____

   _____

   _____

   _____

10. Red blood cells (RBC) lack a nucleus.

    • Predict what limitations this will put on the cell. _____

    _____

    _____

    • Predict why the lack of a nucleus may be advantageous to a RBC. _____

    _____

    _____

11. The hepatocytes of the liver are responsible for detoxifying the blood. Predict which organelle would be more developed in the hepatocytes as compared to a fibrocyte in the dermis.

    _____

    _____

    _____

CELL SHAPES

Cells are categorized into roughly 200 types. Each cell type has a shape that is somewhat unique. For example, skeletal muscle cells are long and cylindrical, neurons may be star-shaped or long and narrow with many branches, and cheek cells, as you have seen, are round and flat. The shape of a cell mirrors the function of the cell. The long, cylindrical muscle cells extend long distances to connect to bones; when the muscle cells perform their primary function of contraction, the connected bones move in response.

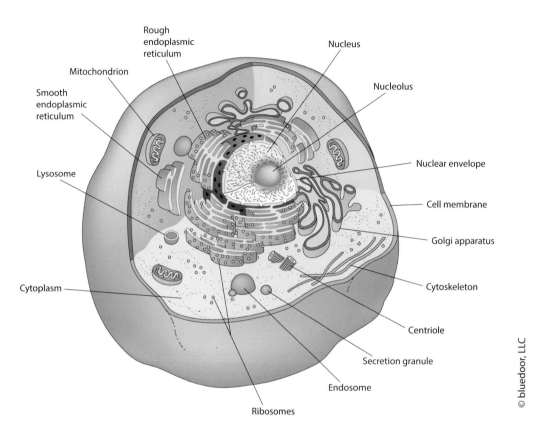

Figure 2.2: Structure of an animal cell.

In the following exercise, you will use the microscope to observe prepared slides of several types of cells, each with a different shape.

Exercise 2.6: Cell Shapes

Obtain your microscope and prepare it for use, following the instructions described previously in this chapter. You will be observing three prepared slides to compare different cell shapes and cell specializations, so obtain prepared slides of skeletal muscle cells, a blood smear, and thick skin.

1. Observe the skeletal muscle cells prepared slide under scanning power first, then switch your objective lens to low power. Notice that the skeletal muscle cells are very long and narrow, and each cell contains many nuclei. Each cell is actually formed by many cells lining up during embryonic development and merging. Because the resulting skeletal muscle cell is very long and narrow, it is referred to as a muscle fiber.

a. What purpose is served by the long length of the muscle fiber? _____

_____

b. What purpose do you think is served by having many nuclei? _____

_____

2. Observe the blood smear prepared slide under scanning power first. Once in focus, switch your objective lens to low power, then to high power. Notice that the blood cells are round, and most do not have a purple-stained nucleus. The abundant cells are red blood cells, and the fewer, larger cells with a single purple-stained nucleus are white blood cells.

a. Compare and contrast the appearance of red blood cells with white blood cells.

_____

b. Suggest a reason why red blood cells lack a nucleus. _____

_____

3. Observe the prepared slide of thick skin under scanning power first. Once in focus, switch to low power and observe the upper layers of cells that form the epidermis of the skin. Once you have found the epidermal layers of cells, switch to high power. Notice that the deep layers of cells are square (three-dimensionally they are cube-shaped, or cuboidal). The cells become more flattened as they approach the surface of the skin. The lowest layer of cells are specialized to produce new cells by the process of cell division, whereas the upper, flatter layers of cells form a protective barrier for the skin.

a. For what function are the upper layers of flattened cells specialized? _____

_____

b. For what function is the deepest layer of cells specialized? _____

_____

4. After you are finished with your microscope observations, always clean up properly:
   - Return slides to appropriate slide tray.
   - Turn off the substage light.
   - Unplug the microscope.
   - If you used oil immersion, clean the slide and objectives with lens paper.
   - Remove the microscope slide and return it to its slide tray.
   - Wrap the electrical cord around the eyepieces.
   - Lower the stage and condenser.
   - Return objective to scanning objective, 4X.
   - **Before you return microscope to the cabinet, let your instructor view your scope.**

TRANSPORT ACROSS THE PLASMA MEMBRANE

The plasma membrane of a cell performs the important function of regulating the movement of substances into and out of the cell. This is possible because the membrane is selectively permeable, allowing some substances to pass through and excluding others. Thus, the plasma membrane represents a partial barrier between the internal environment of the cell and the extracellular environment. These two environments consist of a fluid medium, or solution, while the substances passing through the membrane are particles in solution, or solutes. The tendency of some solutes to pass through while others are excluded establishes a difference in solute concentration between the two sides of the membrane, known as a concentration gradient.

The plasma membrane uses several alternative methods to achieve regulation, which are described in **Table 2.1**. They may be grouped into two categories: **passive processes**, in which energy is not required for the movement, and **active processes**, in which energy is needed for the movement of substances to proceed. Notice from the table that diffusion, facilitated diffusion, osmosis, and filtration are passive processes. Active transport and both forms of vesicular transport are active processes.

Table 2.1: Movement of Materials Across the Plasma Membrane.

Process	Energy Source	Method of Movement	Examples
Diffusion	Passive, by kinetic energy.	Along a concentration gradient.	Movement of oxygen, carbon dioxide, and fats.
Facilitated diffusion	Passive, by kinetic energy.	Along a concentration gradient via a carrier protein.	Movement of glucose into a nutrient-hungry cell.
Osmosis	Passive, by kinetic energy.	Water movement along a concentration gradient.	Movement of water molecules through pores in a membrane.
Filtration	Passive, by kinetic energy.	Along a pressure gradient.	Movement of fluids across membranes forming capillary walls.
Active transport	Cellular energy (ATP).	Against a concentration gradient involving a carrier protein (ion pump).	Movement of glucose and ions against a gradient.
Vesicular transport Endocytosis	Cellular energy (ATP).	Bulk transport of substances into the cell.	Receptor-mediated endocytosis for specific molecules; phagocytosis of dead cells and bacteria by white blood cells; pinocytosis of fluid by various cells.
Exocytosis	Cellular energy (ATP).	Bulk transport of substances out of a cell.	Secretion of hormones by thyroid gland; secretion of digestive enzymes by pancreatic cells.

Exercise 2.7: Osmosis in Live Cells

Osmosis is the primary process of water movement into and out of cells. To better understand osmosis, consider the following scenario:

You're a medical laboratory technician for Oakton Community Hospital. A patient in the Intensive Care Unit has been transfused with the wrong Intravenous (IV) solution. To make matters worse, the IV solution was not labeled. The only known information is what type of solutions are available for use in the ICU. Possible solutions include: 0.9% NaCl, 5% NaCl and 0.4% NaCl. It is your job to determine what type of solution the patient was given and to explain to the nursing staff what happened to the patient's erythrocytes. Complete the following procedure:

> **Materials:** *clean microscope slides and coverslips, animal blood, disposable gloves, 4 disposable pipettes or medicine droppers, 1 test tube, 0.9% saline solution, 5% saline solution, 0.4% NaCl, paper towels, toothpicks, and 10% bleach solution for cleanup.*

1. Once you obtain materials, make predictions with your group members as to which of the solutions are hypertonic, hypotonic and isotonic to cells, and predict the outcome of exposing cells to each solution. Record your hypotheses here: _____

_____

_____

_____

2. Label four microscope slides with the following: 0.9% saline, 5% saline, 0.4% saline, and unknown. With a disposable pipette (or medicine dropper), place a drop of 0.9% saline solution on the 0.9% slide. Dip a toothpick in animal blood and place toothpick to the 0.9% saline solution on the slide and mix gently. Cover the mixture with a coverslip, blot dry, and immediately observe the preparation under high power. Record the shape of the cells and the solution used.

   Cell shape: _____ Solution: _____

   Note that 0.9% saline solution is also called physiological saline, and is balanced to have an equivalent solute concentration with cells. Therefore, this sample represents your control, and the solution is _____ to the cells.

3. With a clean disposable pipette (or medicine dropper), place a drop of 5% saline solution on the 5% slide. Dip a clean toothpick in animal blood, and place toothpick to the 5% saline solution on the slide and mix gently. Cover with a coverslip, and blot dry. Immediately observe the preparation under high power. Record the shape of the cells and the solution used.

   Cell shape: _____ Solution: _____

   The 5% solution is very salty compared to the interior of the cells. In other words, the 5% solution is _____ to the cells, which causes water to exit the cells to give them a shriveled, dehydrated appearance. This effect on cells is called *crenation*, and is shown in **Figure 2.3c**.

4. With a clean disposable pipette (or medicine dropper), place a drop of 0.4% saline solution on the 0.4% slide. Dip a clean toothpick in animal blood, and place toothpick to the 0.4% saline solution on the slide and mix gently. Cover with a coverslip, and blot dry. Immediately observe the preparation under high power. Record the shape of the cells and the solution used.

   Cell shape: _____ Solution: _____

Distilled water contains no salts, so it is _____ to the cells. As a result, water flows into the cells, causing them to swell. Some cells may burst in response to the inflow of water, a phenomenon known as *hemolysis*. Refer to **Figure 2.3b**.

5. Obtain a prepared slide of the patient's blood sample. Assuming the cells still reflect the effect of the original infusion, what type of solution was your patient given? Explain your reasoning.

_____

_____

6. Clean up: Please put glass slides in glass container. All other materials can be disposed of in the garbage. Please clean microscopes and return to the microscope cabinet.

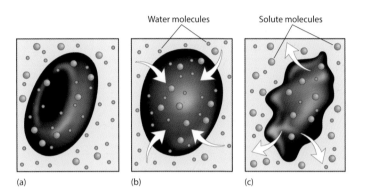

Figure 2.3: Blood cells.

ACTIVE PROCESSES OF MEMBRANE TRANSPORT

Return to **Table 2.1** once more, and notice that several active processes of membrane transport occur. Active processes require an input of energy in the form of ATP to drive the movement across the plasma membrane. The energy is needed to transport substances against a concentration gradient; that is, from a region of low concentration to a region of high concentration. The processes include **active transport**, which involves enzyme action by integral proteins of the membrane, **endocytosis**, in which bulk amounts of substances are taken into the cell by modifying the plasma membrane structure, and **exocytosis**, during which substances are released from the cell into the extracellular environment.

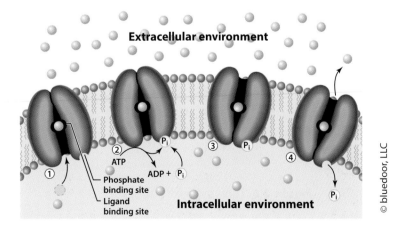

Figure 2.4: Active transport.

Phagocytosis, a mechanism of endocytosis, literally means "the process of cell eating," is the intake of large substances into the cell, followed by internal digestion by cellular enzymes. It requires the cell's plasma membrane to change its shape in order to surround the large substance and engulf it into the cytoplasm. A membranous sac then forms around the substance, called a phagosome, which fuses with a lysosome to digest it. In the human body, phagocytosis is the method in which bacteria and dead cells are removed by specialized white blood cells.

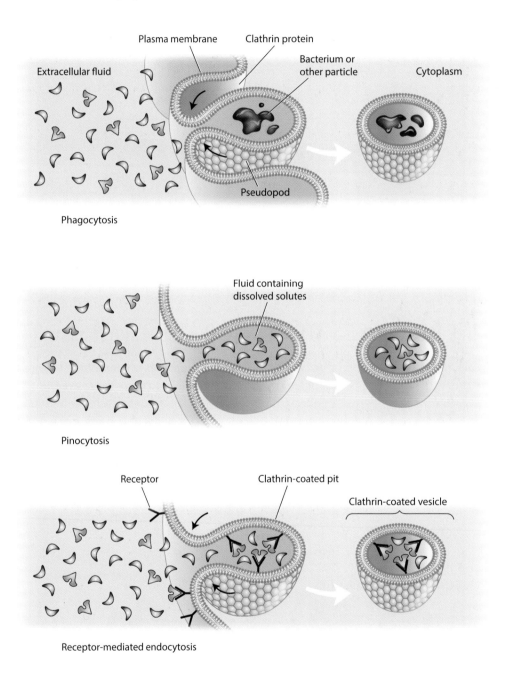

Phagocytosis

Pinocytosis

Receptor-mediated endocytosis

© bluedoor, LLC

Figure 2.5: Three types of Endocytosis.

CHAPTER 2 REVIEW

Name _____

Instructor _____

1. After placing a slide onto a microscope to observe a specimen, you should

   a. turn the light rheostat at high intensity   c. begin at scanning power
   b. begin by using high power   d. make sure the light is turned off

2. When using a microscope and moving the objective lens from low power to high power, it is important to always

   a. focus with the course adjustment knob   c. focus with the fine adjustment knob
   b. focus by moving the condenser upward   d. decrease the light rheostat

3. The total magnification of an object when using high power, assuming the ocular lens power is 10X, is

   a. 100X   c. 1,000X
   b. 400X   d. 40X

4. All cells look alike because

   a. their functions are very similar   c. they all form a part of the body
   b. they all consist of similar architecture   d. incorrect; all cells are not similar

5. The part of a cell that contains attached ribosomes where protein synthesis occurs is the

   a. rough ER   c. mitochondria
   b. smooth ER   d. golgi apparatus

6. The part of the cell that contains enzymes engaged in the production of energy is

   a. rough ER   c. lysosomes
   b. mitochondria   d. nucleus

7. Placing a healthy red blood cell into a solution of 0.9% saline will cause the cell to

   a. burst during hemolysis   c. shrivel during crenation
   b. remain in the healthy state   d. divide into two daughter cells

8. A 10% saline solution is called _____ relative to the interior of a cell.

   a. isotonic   c. hypertonic
   b. hypotonic   d. at equilibrium

APPLYING YOUR NEW KNOWLEDGE

1. A patient was transported to a clinic for treatment following a motorcycle accident, and had lost about 2 pints of blood. The attending nurse provided an intravenous drip with 0.9% saline solution to temporarily maintain blood pressure until a whole blood transfusion could be provided. Explain what would happen to the patient if the 0.9% saline was mistakenly replaced by a 10% saline solution, and why.

MAJOR TYPES OF TISSUE

- Epithelial Tissue
- Connective Tissue
- Muscle Tissue
- Nervous Tissue

A **tissue** is a combination of similar cells that group together to perform a particular function, such as protection, secretion, or contraction. Most complex organisms start out as a single cell, the fertilized egg, which divides until over a trillion cells are produced. During development, these cells specialize into one of four major tissue types: epithelial, connective, muscle, and nervous. Groups of tissues combine to form **organs** which perform specific body functions. It is important to study tissues because they provide the structural and functional basis of organs.

In this chapter, you will learn about each major type of tissue and their most common subtypes by observing prepared slides with the microscope. The study of tissues is called **histology**.

The laboratory exercises in this unit correlate to Chapter 4 in your textbook and to the following BIO 231 course objective:

1. Compare tissue types by anatomy, physiology and location.

   * **NOTE**: The histology figures in this chapter and the histology pictures in your textbook will assist you in the identification of tissues. However, the slides in the slide trays may not look exactly like these pictures. It is important that you learn the characteristics of the tissue and not the staining properties (these properties change from stain to stain).

EPITHELIAL TISSUE

Epithelial tissue or epithelium is distinguished from other tissues by several characteristics:

1. **Cellularity**: Epithelial cells are packed closely together, allowing little or no intercellular material between them. The cells form sheets of cells called membranes that are held together by specialized junctions including tight junctions, gap junctions, and desmosomes.

2. **Avascularity**: The cells are so tightly packed, in fact, that blood vessels cannot pass between them; epithelium is, therefore, an avascular (a = without + vascular = pertaining to small vessels) tissue.

3. **Polarity**: membranes have one free surface called the apical surface which is different from the basal surface.

4. **Regeneration**: well nourished epithelial cells regenerate because they have a high mitotic rate.

The arrangement of cells to form epithelial tissue results in either sheets or clumps of cells. The **sheet-like epithelial tissue** is known as **covering and lining epithelium** which covers the body, lines body cavities and organs, and lines all hollow structures. This type of epithelium serves various functions depending on its location. For example, the body surface is covered by epithelium that protects the body from UV radiation, bacterial invasion, and chemical damage. It also contains sensory receptors. The respiratory tract epithelium is lined with cilia to sweep foreign particles away from the lungs. The small intestine is lined by epithelium that functions in absorption. The kidney tubules contain epithelia that functions in absorption, filtration, and excretion.

Glands are specialized structures arising from epithelium and are formed by localized proliferation and penetration of the epithelial cells into the connective tissue beneath the epithelium. These glands function in secretion of various products and are divided into two major categories: **exocrine glands**, which secrete products into body cavities and surfaces by way of tubular ducts; and **endocrine glands**, whose secretions diffuse into the bloodstream for their transport throughout the body. Exocrine glands are located in the skin (sweat glands), the head (salivary glands), the stomach, mammary glands, prostate gland, liver, and pancreas. Their products include a watery mix of proteins, carbohydrates, or lipids. More specifically, exocrine glands secrete saliva, tears, sweat, oil, bile, pancreatic fluid, sperm, eggs, etc. The endocrine glands include the pituitary gland and the pineal body in the brain, the thymus, the thyroid gland, the parathyroid glands, the pancreas, the adrenal glands, and the gonads (ovaries/testes). The products of endocrine glands are hormones. The study of various exocrine and endocrine glands will be examined in more detail during the study of their respective organ systems.

Epithelium typically lines the inner border of a cavity or lumen of an organ, such as the stomach or the inner aspect of a blood vessel. In most cases, connective tissue underlies the epithelium. The margin of the cell exposed to a body space is called the free or **apical surface**, and the side exposed to the connective tissue layer is the **basal surface**. A thin layer of protein fibers beneath the basal surface connects the epithelial sheet to the underlying connective tissue, and is called the **basement membrane.**

There are many types of epithelial tissues in the body. They are classified according to cell shape and their organization to form either a single layer of cells or multiple layers (**Figure 4.1**). A single layer of cells is called simple epithelium, and a multiple-layered arrangement is called stratified epithelium. **Simple epithelium** provides a partial barrier for diffusion, secretion, absorption, and filtration of selected substances. The two or more layers of cells in **stratified epithelium** create a thicker barrier, providing a protective function.

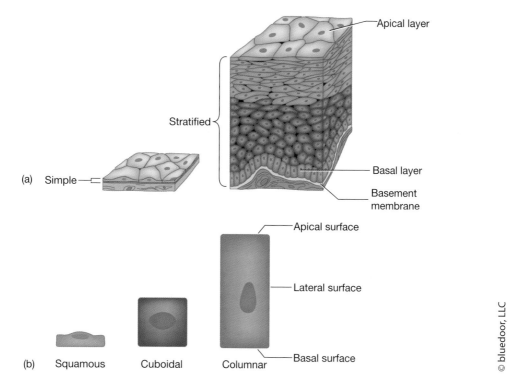

Figure 1.1: Classification of epithelial tissue.

The four alternative shapes of epithelial cells are **squamous**, or flat with a thin nucleus; **cuboidal**, or cube-shaped with a round nucleus near the center of the cell; **columnar**, or tall with an oval nucleus near the basal surface of the cell; and **transitional**, or shape-changing from round, when the tissue is relaxed, to flat, when the tissue is stretched.

You will study the major types of epithelial tissue in the following series of exercises, each of which involves the microscopic examination of prepared slides. The types of epithelium you will observe are simple squamous epithelium, simple cuboidal epithelium, simple columnar epithelium, stratified squamous epithelium, stratified cuboidal epithelium, transitional epithelium, and pseudostratified columnar epithelium.

Microscope Review

When using the microscope in the following exercises, remember the proper handling, care, and use of the microscope in the preceding chapter. Strictly adhere to the following procedures for every microscopic study:

- Always handle the microscope properly and with care.
- Clean lenses only with lens paper before each use.
- Begin any observation with the scanning objective lens.
- Begin focusing with the course adjustment knob.
- After switching to an objective lens with a higher power, use only the fine adjustment knob to focus.

Specific Types of Simple Epithelium (Single Cell Layer Thick)

- Simple Squamous
- Simple Cuboidal
- Simple Columnar
- Pseudostratified Columnar

Exercise 3.1: Simple Squamous Epithelium

Description: Simple squamous epithelium is a single layer of flattened cells with a central disc-shaped nucleus and sparse cytoplasm.

Function: Its very thin structure allows for movement of substances across it during diffusion, filtration, and secretion.

Location: In the ventral cavities, this simple squamous epithelium is referred to as **mesothelium** (in the abdomen forming the epithelium of the serosal or peritoneal membranes); lining the lumen of blood vessels, this type of epithelium is referred to as **endothelium**; lining the cavities of the heart, it's **endocardium**. This epithelium can also be seen surrounding kidney glomeruli and lining aveloi of the lungs.

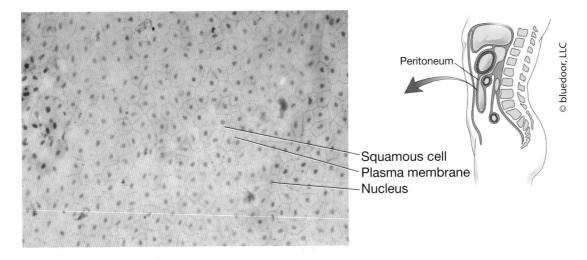

© bluedoor, LLC

Peritoneum

Squamous cell
Plasma membrane
Nucleus

Figure 3.2: Simple squamous epithelium from peritoneum (240X).

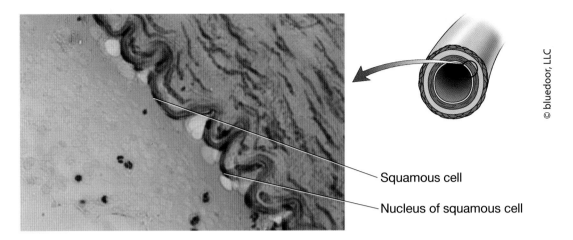

Figure 3.3: Simple squamous epithelium from an artery (400X).

1. Obtain a prepared slide of a cross sectional view of simple squamous epithelium and observe it under high power.
2. Using figure 3.3 as a guide, identify a squamous cell, a nucleus and the cell membrane.
3. Return slide to appropriate slide tray.

Exercise 3.2: Simple Cuboidal Epithelium

Description: Simple cuboidal epithelium is a single layer of cube-shaped cells with large, spherical centrally located nuclei.

Function: Secretion and absorption; often contains cilia or microvilli to assist in these functions.

Location: This tissue forms the walls of small tubes that carry fluids, such as the kidney tubules and ducts of certain glands, covers the surface of the ovary, and makes up the secreting portion of some endocrine glands.

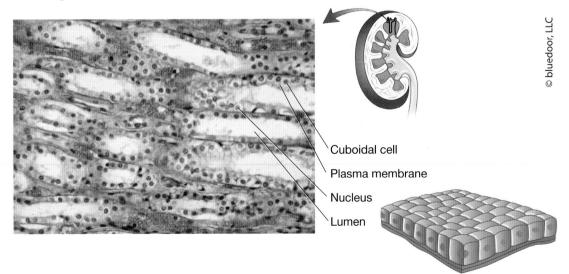

Figure 3.4: Simple cuboidal epithelium in kidney tubule (400X).

1. Obtain a prepared slide of simple cuboidal epithelium and observe it under high power.

2. Using **Figure 3.4** as a guide, identify a cuboidal cell, the plasma membrane, a nucleus, and a lumen. Also, identify the apical surface and basal surface of a cell. Finally, identify connective tissue in your viewing area.

3. Return slide to appropriate slide tray.

Exercise 3.3: Simple Columnar Epithelium

Description: A single layer of tall, usually cylindrical cells. The round to oval nucleus is near the basal surface of each cell. In some parts of the body, the epithelium includes unicellular exocrine glands between the cylindrical cells, known as *goblet cells,* which produce and secrete mucus. There are two types of simple columnar epithelia: nonciliated and ciliated. Nonciliated simple columnar epithelium is much more common.

Location and Function of Nonciliated Simple Columnar Epithelium: Forms an inner lining of the digestive tract (stomach to anal canal), reproductive tract (excluding the fallopian tubes and portions of the uterus), urinary tracts, and the excretory ducts of many glands. It often contains microvilli at the apical surface of cells, which aid in secretion and absorption.

Location and Function of Ciliated Simple Columnar Epithelium: Lines portions of the respiratory tract (smaller bronchi), the fallopian tubes, and parts of the uterus, the paranasal sinuses, and the central canal of the spinal cord. Its cilia propel mucus, cerebrospinal fluid, and reproductive cells.

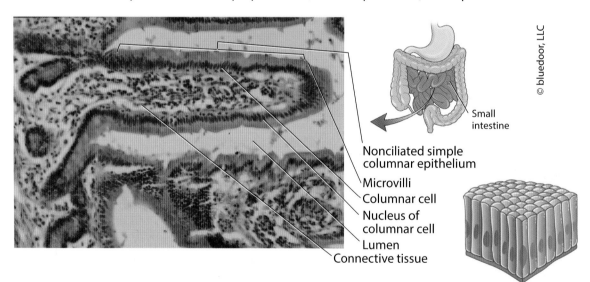

© bluedoor, LLC

Small intestine

Nonciliated simple columnar epithelium

Microvilli

Columnar cell

Nucleus of columnar cell

Lumen

Connective tissue

Figure 3.5: Simple columnar epithelium, nonciliated, of the small intestine (250X)

1. Obtain a prepared slide of simple columnar epithelium and observe it under high power.

2. Using **Figure 3.5** as a guide, identify the nonciliated simple columnar epithelium, a columnar cell, and connective tissue.

3. The thin band of microvilli is called the brush border. The microvilli increase the surface area of the small intestinal lining.

4. Return slide to appropriate slide tray.

Exercise 3.4: Pseudostratified Columnar Epithelium

Description: Pseudostratified (pseudo = false + stratified = layer) columnar epithelium is a tissue that appears to have many layers, but, in fact, has only one. The presence of one layer versus multiple layers is determined by cell contact with the basement membrane. In this tissue, all cells contact the basement membrane, giving it the classification of a single layer. The misleading appearance of many layers is due to the varying shape of the cells: some are uniformly cylindrical, while others narrowly twist and turn at different angles through the tissue, and yet others are short and do not contribute to the apical surface of the tissue. Pseudostratified columnar epithelium may be ciliated or nonciliated.

Location and Function of Ciliated Pseudostratified Columnar Epithelium: The ciliated form is abbreviated PSCC epithelium, and is found lining the trachea and bronchi. Its cilia beat rhythmically to move a stream of mucus upward toward the mouth and nasal cavity; mucus-secreting goblet cells are common in this tissue.

Location and Function of Nonciliated Pseudostratified Columnar Epithelium: The nonciliated form lacks both cilia and goblet cells, and is found lining large ducts of certain glands, the epididymis, and part of the male urethra.

You will observe only pseudostratified ciliated columnar epithelium in this exercise.

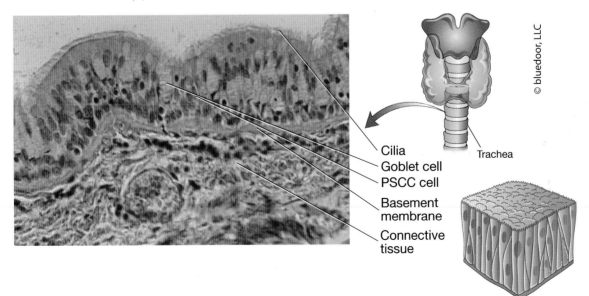

Cilia
Goblet cell
PSCC cell
Basement membrane
Connective tissue

Trachea

© bluedoor, LLC

Figure 3.6: Pseudostratified ciliated columnar epithelium from the trachea (400X).

1. Obtain a prepared slide pseudostratified columnar epithelium and view under high power.

2. Observe the image under high power. Using **Figure 3.6** as a guide, identify cilia, a goblet cell, PSCC cell, and connective tissue.

3. Return slide to appropriate slide tray.

Specific Types of Stratified Epithelium

- Stratified Squamous
- Stratified Cuboidal
- Stratified Columnar
- Transitional

Exercise 3.5: Stratified Squamous Epithelium

Description: Stratified squamous epithelium is a tissue composed of many layers of cells. The superficial cells are squamous (flat), while the cells in the deepest layers are columnar or cuboidal. Between the two layers, the cells transition from columnar or cuboidal to squamous.

Function: The multiple layers of this tissue provide it with an important role in protection of underlying tissues. In some parts of the body, the squamous layer of cells is filled with the tough protein keratin, which provides an added protective benefit.

Location: Stratified squamous epithelium forms the epidermis of the skin and lines the entry portals of the body.

In this exercise, you will observe two examples of stratified squamous epithelium: in the epidermis, where the tissue is keratinized, and in the esophagus, where it is nonkeratinized.

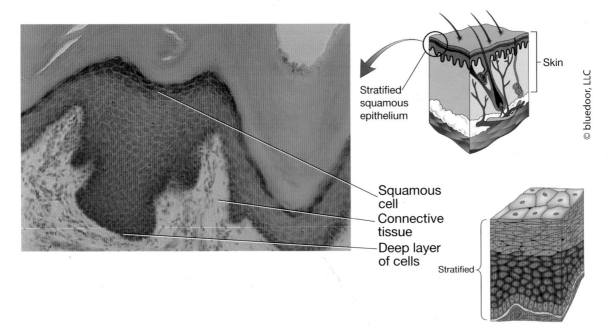

Figure 3.7: Stratified squamous epithelium from skin, keratinized (250X).

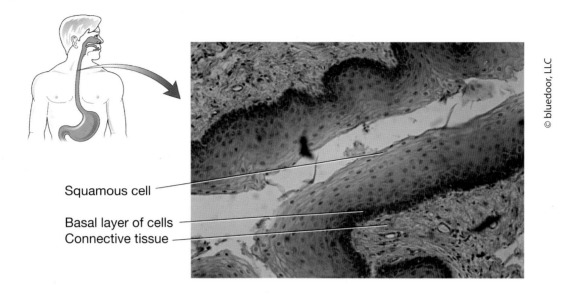

Squamous cell

Basal layer of cells

Connective tissue

© bluedoor, LLC

Figure 3.8: Stratified squamous epithelium from the esophagus, nonkeratinized (250X)

1. Obtain a prepared slide of a section through the skin. Under scanning power, find the superficial epidermis, which appears as the purple or orange stained area adjacent to the surface; then observe under low power.

2. Using **Figure 3.7** as a guide, identify the deep layer of cells, superficial layer of cells, a squamous cell, and connective tissue.

3. Return slide to appropriate slide tray.

Exercise 3.6: Stratified Cuboidal Epithelium

Description: Two layers of cubelike cells.

Function: Protection

Location: Mammary glands, salivary glands, and largest ducts of sweat glands.

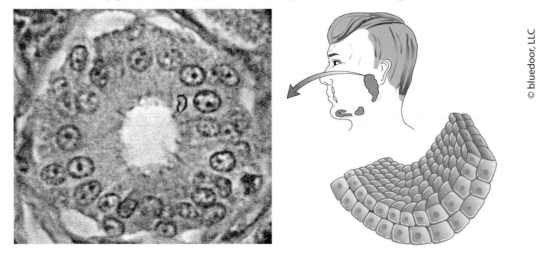

© bluedoor, LLC

Figure 3.9: Stratified cuboidal epithelium forming a salivary gland duct.

Exercise 3.7: Transitional Epithelium

Description: Transitional epithelial tissue has been given its name because the cells are usually in the process of changing between a relaxed, plump state and a compressed, flattened state. The change allows the tissue to stretch.

Location and Function: It is found lining the urinary bladder and portions of the ureter and urethra, which must stretch to accommodate a temporary increase in urine volume, then return to their original, empty state. During stretching, the apical layer of cells in the tissue flattens and the number of cell layers decreases. When the tissue relaxes, the apical layer of cells become plump and round.

In this exercise, you will observe transitional epithelium from the urinary bladder that is in the relaxed state.

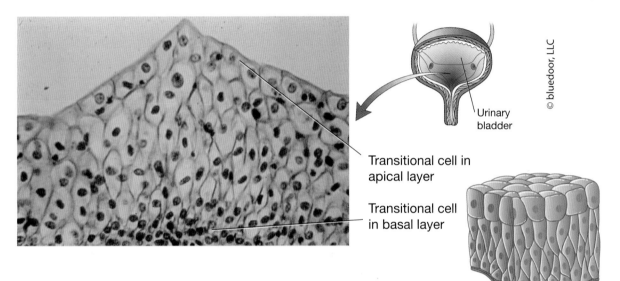

Urinary bladder

Transitional cell in apical layer

Transitional cell in basal layer

© bluedoor, LLC

Figure 3.10: Transitional epithelium (relaxed) from the urinary bladder (400X)

CONNECTIVE TISSUE

Connective tissue is the most abundant and widely distributed type of tissue in the body. During embryonic development, all adult forms of connective tissue arise in the form of dispersed cells in a protein and fluid matrix. This early connective tissue is called **mesenchyme**. Later, **mesenchyme** gives rise to the connective tissue types that you will observe in the lab: loose connective tissue, dense connective tissue, cartilage, bone, and blood.

Exercise 3.8: Mesenchyme (Embryonic Connective Tissue)

Description: Mesenchyme has gel-like ground substance containing fibers and star-shaped mesenchymal cells.

Function: Gives rise to all other connective tissue types.

Location: Embryo.

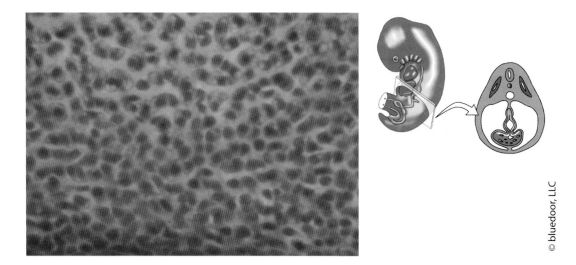

© bluedoor, LLC

Figure 3.11: Mesenchymal tissue (embyronic connective tissue)

Major Types of Connective Tissue

- Loose Connective Tissue
- Dense Connective Tissue
- Cartilage
- Bone
- Blood

All **connective tissues** has the same basic components including living cells and nonliving extracellular material. The **cells** include *fibroblasts* (dense and loose connective tissue), *chondroblasts* and *chondrocytes* (cartilage), *osteoblasts* and *osteocytes* (bone), and *hematopoietic stem cells* (blood). The extracellular material includes protein fibers and ground substance. The **protein fibers** include *collagen (white) fibers, elastic (yellow) fibers,* and *reticular (fine collagen) fibers.* The fibers provide support. The **ground substance** is composed of *interstitial fluid, cell adhesion proteins,* and *proteoglycans.* Depending on the relative amounts of those components, the ground substance is *fluid, semifluid, gelatinous, or hard.* The ground substance provides support and serves as a medium of transport for nutrients and dissolved substances. With the exception of blood, the cells produce the protein fibers and ground substance for the major types of connective tissue. With the exception of cartilage which is avascular and tendons and ligaments which are poorly vascularized, all other types of connective tissue have a rich supply of blood vessels.

The **density** of protein fibers and ground substance in connective tissue varies from one type to another. For example, **loose connective tissue** consists of a low density of protein fibers within a semifluid ground substance, while **dense connective tissue** has a much higher density of protein fibers that allow a sparse amount of semifluid ground substance. Also, **cartilage** has a relatively dense protein matrix, and its ground substance is gelatinous due to the presence of many large protein-sugar molecules. **Bone**, of course, has a very hard ground substance, due to the abundance of minerals. Its protein matrix is mostly collagen, which provides a substrate for the hard minerals. **Blood** is very different, with a population of cells carried in a fluid ground substance, known as plasma.

Each type of connective tissue has its own particular function, but the function of all connective tissues, in general, is to connect and support the tissues and organs of the body. **Connective tissue** provides a continuity of form, providing the support needed for other body functions to proceed. Some of the more specific functions will be described throughout this section, and include protection, support, insulation, transportation, participation in movement, storage of minerals, and energy storage.

Specific Types of Loose Connective Tissue

- Areolar Tissue
- Adipose Tissue
- Reticular Tissue

Exercise 3.9: Loose Connective Tissue

Loose connective tissue is characterized by the presence of protein fibers that are loosely arranged and in low abundance. Its primary cell type is the **fibroblast**, which is a large cell capable of movement throughout the semifluid ground substance. Fibroblasts are productive cells, secreting the protein fibers of the loose matrix and many of the ground substance molecules. Often, loose connective tissue is an important thoroughfare for blood vessels, lymphatics, and nerves coursing through the body. There are several main types of loose connective tissue including **areolar tissue, adipose tissue,** and **reticular tissue.**

A. Areolar Tissue

Areolar tissue is considered the prototype of the connective tissues because it is the best representative of the common structural plan of all the connective tissues. It is found between the skin and muscles and between other organs of the body, acting as a soft packing tissue. It forms the **lamina propria** of mucous membranes and surrounds capillaries.

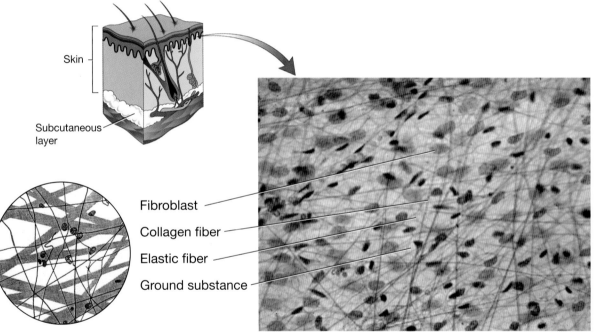

Skin

Subcutaneous layer

Fibroblast

Collagen fiber

Elastic fiber

Ground substance

© bluedoor, LLC

Figure 3.12: Areolar tissue, a form of loose connective tissue.

1. Obtain a prepared slide of **areolar tissue** (also called areolar loose connective tissue). At scanning power, find areolar tissue as the area immediately deep to a layer of epithelium. Observe areolar tissue under high power.

2. As you observe the areolar tissue specimen, notice the large cells that often include processes; these are the fibroblasts. **Fibroblasts** are the cell type that secretes the matrix in areolar tissue. Other cells that may be present are **mast cells** which have large, darkly stained granules in their cytoplasm. Mast cells release histamine which makes capillaries more permeable during inflammatory reactions and allergies and are partly responsible for the "runny nose" of allergies.

White blood cells and large macrophages, which remove unwanted substances by **phagocytosis**, are also present in areolar tissue. Areolar tissue contains all three types of fibers. The thick bands are collagen fibers, and the thinner black strands are elastic fibers. Reticular fibers are present but may be too fine to see. The ground substance of areolar tissue is gel-like.

3. Using **Figure 3.12** as a reference, identify a fibroblast, collagen fiber, elastic fiber, and ground substance.

4. Return slide to appropriate slide tray.

B. Adipose Tissue

Adipose tissue is a highly specialized form of loose connective tissue. Its dominant cells are **adipocytes**, which are capable of housing a very large volume of lipid molecules. The lipids are an efficient means of storing energy. Adipose tissue is also an efficient insulating blanket, and a cushion that protects from injury. It is mainly found associated with areolar tissue between the skin and muscles, forming the subcutaneous fat of the **superficial fascia.** It is also found around the eyes, in the breasts, abdomen, and around certain visceral organs, such as the kidneys, heart, and spleen.

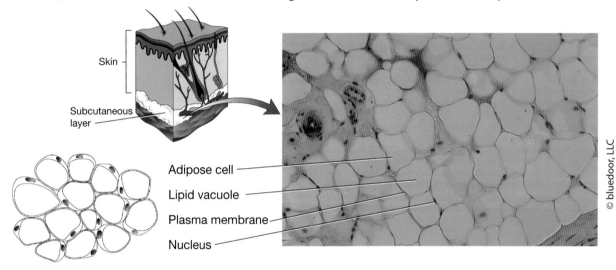

Figure 3.13: Adipose tissue (400X).

1. Obtain a prepared slide of adipose tissue.

2. At low power, observe the large open circles. Each circle is a section through an adipose cell. Look carefully at high power and notice a small bump on the plasma membrane of each cell: this is the nucleus and most of the cytoplasm. The large area surrounded by the plasma membrane that appears like an empty space is a vacuole filled with lipids.

3. Using **Figure 3.13** as a guide, identify the adipose cell, plasma membrane, and nucleus of adipose cell.

4. Return slide to appropriate slide tray.

C. Reticular Connective Tissue

Reticular connective tissue is dominated by thin, branching reticular fibers and loose ground substance. The fibers and ground substance are produced by **reticular cells,** which are a specialized type of fibroblast. Reticular connective tissue forms an internal scaffolding for certain organs, such as lymph nodes, bone marrow, and the spleen. This scaffolding supports other cell types including **white blood cells, mast cells,** and **macrophages.**

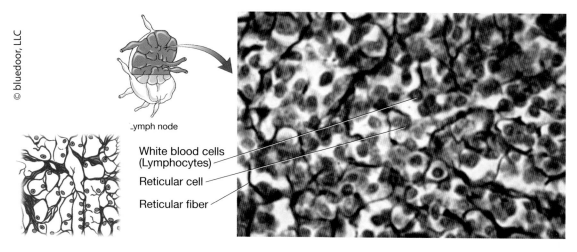

Lymph node

White blood cells
(Lymphocytes)

Reticular cell

Reticular fiber

Figure 3.14: Reticular connective tissue from the spleen (400X).

Specific Types of Dense Connective Tissue

- Dense Regular Connective Tissue (tendon, ligament)

- Dense Irregular Connective Tissue

- Elastic Connective Tissue

Exercise 3.10: Dense Connective Tissue

Dense connective tissue is characterized by a high concentration of collagen fibers, allowing relatively little ground substance and few cells. Due to the dominance of the collagen fibers, it is also called **fibrous connective tissue.** The cells are **fibroblasts,** which produce the collagen fibers and ground substance. There are three distinct types of dense connective tissue: dense regular, dense irregular, and elastic connective tissue. **Dense regular connective tissue** has a roughly parallel arrangement of collagen fibers that form tendons, ligaments, and aponeuroses. **Dense irregular connective tissue** has a random arrangement of fibers and is found in the deep layer of the skin (the dermis), in the sclera of the eyes, in the fascia in and around muscles, in fibrous capsules surrounding many organs, in the submucosa of the digestive tracts, and in the valves and pericardium of the heart. **Elastic connective tissue** also has a dense arrangement of collagen fibers, but it is dominated by a large number of branching elastic fibers. **Elastic connective tissue** is found in the walls of large arteries, where it provides a firm, but elastic, structure. All three forms of dense connective tissue provide strength with some flexibility.

A. Dense Regular Connective Tissue

In this exercise, you will observe dense regular connective tissue by examining a section through a tendon, which connects muscle to bone. You may also observe this tissue in a prepared slide of a ligament, which connects a bone to another bone.

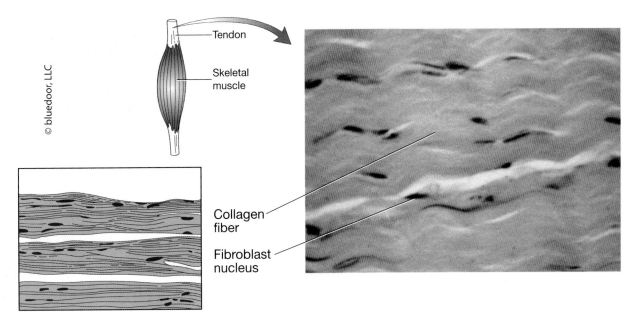

Figure 3.15: Dense regular connective tissue from a tendon.

1. Obtain a prepared slide of a sectioned **tendon** under high power. Observe the regular, mostly parallel arrangement of pink-stained collagen fibers. The **fibroblasts** are visible as the small, purple-stained nuclei between the thick collagen strands.

2. Using **Figure 3.15** as a guide, identify a collagen fiber and fibroblast nucleus under low power:

3. Return slide to appropriate slide tray.

B. Dense Irregular Connective Tissue

You have learned that **dense irregular connective tissue** consists of a random arrangement of collagen fibers, which dominate the tissue. In this exercise, you will study a prepared slide of the skin. The deep layer of the skin, the dermis, provides an excellent example of dense irregular connective tissue.

1. Obtain a prepared slide of a section through the **skin**. Under scanning power, locate the region of the skin beneath the epithelial layer, which appears primarily pink from the abundance of collagen fibers. Examine this part of the skin under high power more carefully, and notice the nonparallel arrangement of collagen fibers that characterize this tissue. The tissue includes **fibroblasts**, which produce the fibers and semifluid ground substance, and **macrophages**. Notice the presence of glandular tissue and blood vessels.

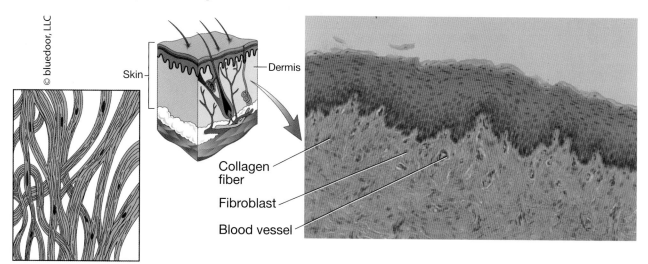

© bluedoor, LLC

Skin

Dermis

Collagen fiber

Fibroblast

Blood vessel

Figure 3.16: Dense irregular connective tissue from the dermis of the skin (200X).

2. Using **Figure 3.16** as a reference, locate the dense irregular connective tissue under high power. Identify collagen fiber, fibroblast, and blood vessel.

3. Return slide to appropriate slide tray.

Specific Types of Cartilage

- Hyaline Cartilage
- Fibrocartilage
- Elastic Cartilage

Exercise 3.11: Cartilage

Unlike other forms of connective tissue, **cartilage** has a gelatinous ground substance. The ground substance is strengthened by the presence of protein fibers, including collagen fibers and elastic fibers, giving cartilage some flexibility and resistance to stress. The ground substance and fibers are produced by active cells known as **chondroblasts**, which become isolated in spaces known as lacunae (lacunae = little lakes; la-KOO-na) to eventually transform into mature chondrocytes. The center of the cartilage is avascular, due to the density of the ground substance and protein matrix. However, it is surrounded by a region of protein fibers and blood vessels known as the **perichondrium** (peri- = around + chondr = cartilage + -ium = pertaining to), which serves as the source of nourishing interstitial fluid for the embedded chondrocytes. Cartilage is the prominent tissue in joints throughout the body, and includes three types: **hyaline cartilage, fibrocartilage,** and **elastic cartilage.**

A. Hyaline Cartilage

Hyaline cartilage forms most of the embryonic skeleton. In the adult, it is the glassy, bluish-white material at the ends of long bones, which serves as a smooth surface to support bone movement at many of the body's joints. It is also present in the trachea, where it forms the rings that keep the trachea open. In addition, it forms costal cartilages of the ribs, cartilages of the nose, and larynx. Hyaline cartilage has resilient cushioning properties and resists compressive stress. The ground substance of hyaline cartilage is filled with large protein-sugar molecules called **chondroitin sulfate,** which mask the collagen fibers weaving through it. In this exercise, you will examine a sectioned specimen of hyaline cartilage taken from the trachea.

© bluedoor, LLC

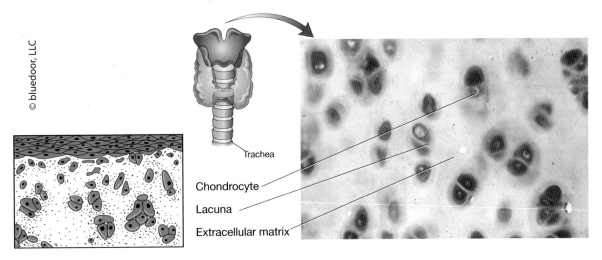

Trachea

Chondrocyte

Lacuna

Extracellular matrix

Figure 3.18: Hyaline cartilage from the trachea, high power (400X).

1. Obtain a prepared slide of a section through the **trachea.** Under scanning power, find the area in the center of the tracheal wall that appears purplish in color. This is **hyaline cartilage.** Still under scanning power, notice the band of collagen fibers surrounding the hyaline cartilage center. This band is the **perichondrium**. Study this tissue under high power, and notice that you are unable to see individual collagen fibers in the center area of hyaline cartilage. Although the collagen fibers are present, they are hidden from view by the dense ground substance. Also, notice the **chondrocytes** embedded within lacunae. These are often found in pairs.

2. Using **Figure 3.18** as a reference, locate the hyaline cartilage under high power. Identify a chondrocyte, lacuna, and extracellular matrix.

3. Return slide to appropriate tray.

B. Fibrocartilage

Fibrocartilage is a dense, slightly flexible cartilage that contains bundles of collagen fibers in the extracellular matrix. The ground substance contains less chondroitin sulfate than hyaline cartilage, allowing the collagen fibers to become visible as thin wavy lines. Similar to hyaline cartilage, its **chondrocytes** lie within lacunae. Fibrocartilage has tensile strength with the ability to absorb compressive shock. It is present in certain joints, such as the pubic symphysis where the hip bones meet anteriorly, the intervertebral discs located between vertebrae in the spinal column, and it forms the meniscus pads in the knees.

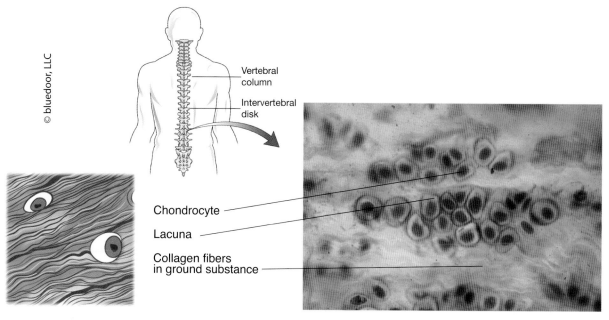

© bluedoor, LLC

Vertebral column

Intervertebral disk

Chondrocyte

Lacuna

Collagen fibers in ground substance

Figure 3.19: Fibrocartilage from an intervertebral disc (400X)

1. Obtain a prepared slide of **fibrocartilage**, taken either from the symphysis pubis or from an intervertebral disc. In some slides of fibrocartilage, the tissue is stained blue in order to highlight the collagen fibers. In others, the collagen fibers are a blur of pink. The **chondrocytes** should appear stained pink. Observe fibrocartilage under high power.

2. Using **Figure 3.19** as a guide, under high power identify chondrocyte, lacuna, and collagen fibers in ground substance.

3. Return slide to appropriate slide tray.

C. Elastic Cartilage

Elastic cartilage is a yellowish cartilage characterized by the presence of elastic fibers that dominate the protein matrix. The thin, branching elastic fibers can be observed in a prepared slide under the microscope. Similar to other cartilages, it contains chondroitin sulfate in the ground substance and chondrocytes within lacunae. Elastic cartilage is a flexible tissue that supports the framework of the ears, the end of the nose, and the lid between the pharynx and the larynx called the epiglottis.

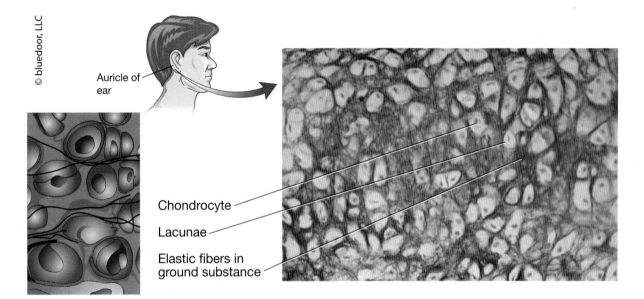

© bluedoor, LLC

Auricle of ear

Chondrocyte

Lacunae

Elastic fibers in ground substance

Figure 3.20: Elastic cartilage from the ear auricle (400X).

1. Obtain a prepared slide of **elastic cartilage,** taken either from the ear or epiglottis. Find the cartilage under scanning power, and then study the features of elastic cartilage under high power. Note the elastic fibers that appear as thin black, branching lines in the matrix.

2. Using **Figure 3.20** as a guide, under high power identify a chondrocyte, lacuna, and elastic fibers in ground substance.

3. Return slide to appropriate slide tray.

Specific Types of Bone

- Compact Bone
- Spongy Bone

Exercise 3.12: Bone Tissue

Bone, or osseous, tissue is a form of connective tissue with a hard, calcified extracellular matrix. The hardness that characterizes it provides protection to underlying tissues and organs. Bone also supports other tissues, stores mineral salts made up of calcium and phosphates, participates in body movement by its attachment to muscles, and contains red marrow where blood cells are manufactured (hematopoiesis) and released into the bloodstream. Its extracellular matrix consists of inorganic salts, including calcium phosphate, that provides a hard quality and collagen fibers that provide strength and some flexibility. The matrix is organized in layers like those of an onion, called **lamellae**. Bone tissue is well vascularized.

Bone tissue is produced by mobile bone cells called **osteoblasts** (osteo = bone + -blast = developing). As new bone is produced, the osteoblasts cement themselves into lacunae, and become immobile. These immobile, mature bone cells are **osteocytes**. The osteocytes receive nourishing interstitial fluid by way of diffusion through tiny canals that penetrate the lamellae, known as **canaliculi**, allowing the entombed cells to communicate with one another and a central canal that transmits blood vessels, called the **osteonic (central) canal**.

In this exercise, you will study a prepared slide of compact bone, which has been dried to remove it of much of its organic components. This process improves the clarity of the specimen for study.

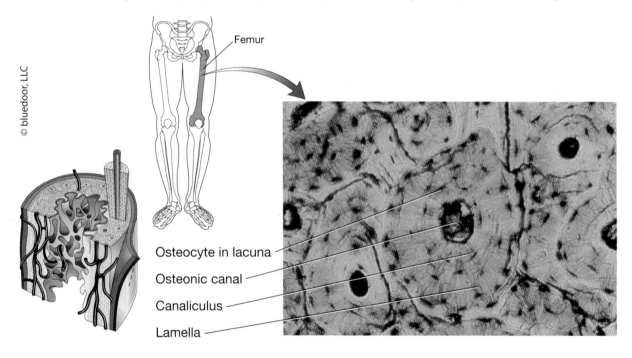

Femur

Osteocyte in lacuna

Osteonic canal

Canaliculus

Lamella

Figure 3.21: Compact bone from a femur (400X).

1. Obtain a prepared slide of dried bone tissue.

2. Using the scanning objective, identify osteonic canals.

3. Under low magnification (10x), identify lacuna, lamellae and canaliculi.

4. Return slide to appropriate slide tray.

Specific Types of Blood

- Red Blood Cells
- White Blood Cells

Exercise 3.13: Blood

It may surprise you to learn that **blood** is a type of connective tissue. It is the most fluid of the connective tissues, with a ground substance, called plasma that is only slightly thicker than water. Proteins are present, but their quantity is very small compared to other connective tissues. The cells of blood are referred to as **formed elements**, and include **red blood cells, white blood cells,** and fragments of cells known as **platelets**. The blood performs the vital function of transporting oxygen and carbon dioxide to and from body cells, and waste materials, hormones, enzymes, nutrients, and other vital materials throughout the body. In this brief exercise, you will observe a sample of blood, called a blood smear that has been prepared with stain to highlight the cells.

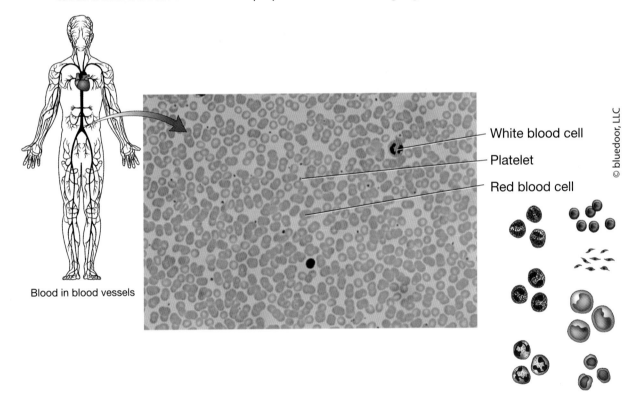

Blood in blood vessels

White blood cell

Platelet

Red blood cell

© bluedoor, LLC

Figure 3.22: A blood smear (400X).

1. Obtain a prepared slide of a blood smear, and observe it under high power.
2. Identify red blood cells, white blood cells, and platelets.
3. Return slide to appropriate slide tray.

MUSCLE TISSUE

Muscle tissue consists of specialized cells containing molecular filaments of protein. The proteins are mainly **myosin** and **actin**, which are arranged in parallel bundles. The protein filaments enable the cells to shorten in length, or contract. Contraction of many cells in a coordinated manner causes the movement of body parts. Thus, muscle tissue functions in body movement. Because muscle contraction produces heat as a byproduct, muscle tissue also contributes to temperature regulation.

There are three types of muscle tissue. Skeletal muscle tissue is the type that is attached to bones, and is the primary tissue of the muscular system. **Skeletal muscle cells**, or muscle fibers, are extremely long and cylindrical in shape. Each contains many nuclei, and crossbands that run perpendicular to the fiber length producing a striped appearance, known as striations. Contraction of skeletal muscle is controlled by the conscious brain, or is voluntary. It results in the movement of bones to provide skeletal movement. **Smooth muscle tissue** forms sheets that contribute to the walls of hollow organs, such as blood vessels, stomach, and small intestine. Its cells are spindle-shaped with a single nucleus, and lack striations. Smooth muscle contraction propels substances through the hollow organs, and is involuntarily controlled by the brain. The third type of muscle tissue is **cardiac muscle tissue,** which forms the wall of the heart. Cardiac muscle cells are quadrangular in shape, contain striations, and also contain thickenings at the junction between adjacent cells (gap junctions), where they are called intercalated discs. Cardiac muscle cells are usually uninucleate. Cardiac muscle contraction is involuntary, propelling blood forward.

Specific Types of Muscle Tissue

- Skeletal Muscle
- Cardiac Muscle
- Smooth Muscle

Exercise 3.14: Skeletal Muscle Tissue

You will observe a prepared slide of skeletal muscle tissue.

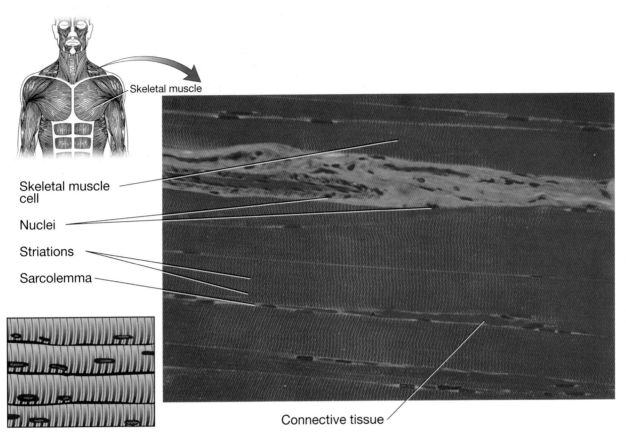

Skeletal muscle

Skeletal muscle cell

Nuclei

Striations

Sarcolemma

Connective tissue

Figure 3.23: Skeletal muscle tissue from a skeletal muscle (400X).

1. Obtain a slide of **skeletal muscle tissue** and first observe it under low power. Under low power, skeletal muscle tissue appears like long, narrow strands of pink-stained cells that extend parallel to one another. Observe the tissue more carefully under high power by focusing on several cells, or fibers. Notice the presence of connective tissue between the muscle fibers.

2. Using **Figure 3.23** as a reference, under high power, identify a skeletal muscle cell, nuclei, striations, and connective tissue.

3. Return slide to appropriate slide tray.

Exercise 3.15: Cardiac Muscle Tissue

You will observe a prepared slide of a section through the heart wall. The layer of **cardiac muscle** in the heart is called the **myocardium**.

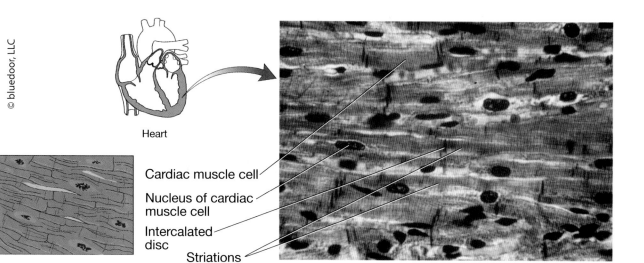

Figure 3.24: Cardiac muscle tissue from the heart wall (400X).

1. Obtain a prepared slide of a section through the **heart wall** that includes the **myocardium**. Under low power, find the area of the specimen containing cardiac muscle tissue by looking for a large region of pink-stained cells that fit tightly together. Under high power, observe an area of cardiac muscle cells.

2. Using **Figure 3.24** as a reference, under high power, identify cardiac muscle cell, nucleus, striations, and intercalated disc.

3. Return slide to appropriate slide tray.

Exercise 3.16: Smooth Muscle Tissue

You will observe a prepared slide of a cross section through a **hollow visceral organ**, such as an artery, the stomach, or the small intestine, in order to study smooth muscle tissue.

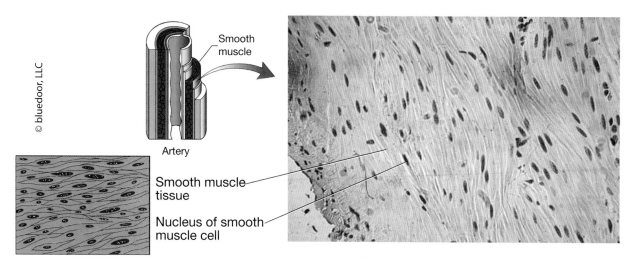

Figure 3.25: Smooth muscle tissue from the wall of a large artery (400X).

1. Obtain a prepared slide containing **smooth muscle tissue.** Find the smooth muscle tissue under low power by looking for a layer of cells in the wall of the organ that is dominated by pink-stained cells. Study the tissue more carefully under high power. The smooth muscle cells are spindle-shaped (long and narrow that taper to pointed ends), have a single nucleus, and fit tightly together.

2. Using **Figure 3.25** as a reference, under high power, identify a smooth muscle cell and the nucleus of a smooth muscle cell.

3. Return slide to appropriate tray.

NERVOUS TISSUE

Nervous tissue, or neural tissue, differs from the other types of tissues by the presence of cells that are highly specialized to communicate to other cells by **electrochemical signals.** This specialized property is known as **conductivity.** The cells are called neurons, which populate the brain, spinal cord, and nerves. **Neurons** are found in many different shapes, most of which contain a long process called an axon, which conducts the signal to another cell, and smaller processes called dendrites, which receive signals from other cells. In addition to neurons, nervous tissue includes cells that support neurons, called **neuroglia**. In most organs containing nervous tissue, the neuroglia outnumber neurons by roughly ten to one.

Specific Types of Nervous Tissue

- Neurons
- Neuroglia

Exercise 3.17: Nervous Tissue

A prepared specimen of nervous tissue from the spinal cord or brain will be studied in this exercise.

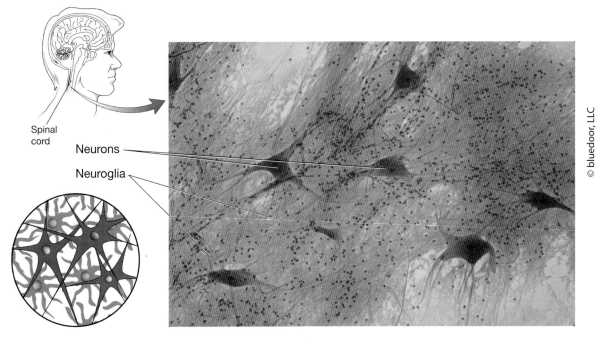

© bluedoor, LLC

Figure 3.26: Nervous tissue from the spinal cord (400X).

1. Obtain a prepared slide of **nervous tissue.** Using low power, find neurons by looking for large cells with numerous processes that are stained darker than surrounding structures. Switch to high power and study the neurons more closely. Also under high power, identify neuroglia as smaller cells with little or no visible processes. Use **Figure 3.26** as a guide.

2. Return slide to appropriate slide tray.

MEMBRANES

The **membranes** of the body form protective sheets that transmit blood vessels, lymphatic vessels, and nerves. They cover surfaces and line cavities throughout the body. Membranes are divided into two categories: **epithelial membranes** and **synovial membranes.**

Epithelial membranes are composed of one or more layers of epithelial cells bound to an underlying layer of connective tissue. They include three types:

- **Cutaneous membrane** is the skin, or integument. It is the only epithelial membrane that does not secrete a lubricating fluid, since the epithelium is the keratinizing stratified squamous epithelium of the epidermis.

- **Mucous membranes** line the body cavities that open to the exterior including the digestive tract, respiratory tract, and urogenital tracts. In the digestive and respiratory tracts, the epithelium secretes mucus, which is a viscous, sticky fluid. In the urogenital tract, these membranes are kept wet by urine and other secretions. The epithelium of mucous membranes is stratified to provide a protective function, which is aided by the thick, sticky mucus. Beneath the epithelium is a layer of loose connective tissue, known as the **lamina propria.** Mucous membranes are also known as **mucosae**.

- **Serous membranes** line body cavities and cover the surfaces of many internal organs. The epithelium is usually a single layer of squamous cells (simple squamous epithelium, in the abdomen called mesothelium), which is associated with a small amount of areolar tissue. The epithelial cells produce a watery lubricating fluid called **serous fluid.** Serous membranes are also known as **serosae**. Serosae that lines body cavities is called the **parietal layer**. The parietal layer is continuous with the **visceral layer**, which is the layer that covers the organs. These double-layered serosae secrete **serous fluid**. Serous fluid is a thin fluid that lubricates the body cavity walls and organs to reduce friction internally. Inflammation of these membranes, as in peritonitis, can give rise to severe pain. Serous membranes also line the inside of blood vessels and the heart. Here, the serous membranes have special names. Serous membranes lining blood vessels are called **endothelium**, while those lining the inside of the heart are called **endocardium**. Capillary walls are made completely of a selectively permeable serous membrane that separates the blood and extracellular fluid of the body.

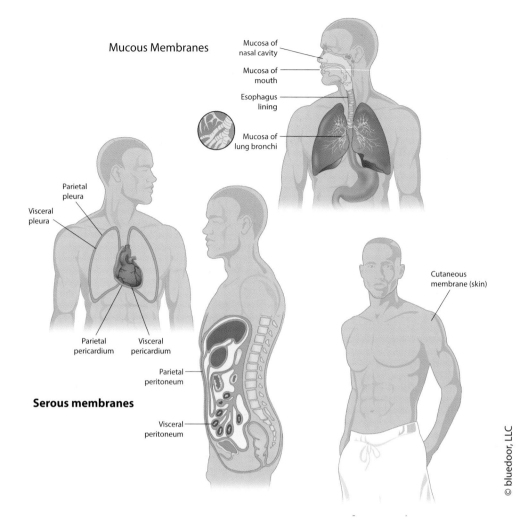

Figure 3.27: Epithelial membranes.

Synovial membranes differ from epithelial membranes because they are composed entirely of connective tissue. Thus, they contain no epithelial cells. They line the cavities surrounding the joints, forming a smooth surface and a lubricating fluid (**synovial fluid**). They also line tendon sheaths and bursae (small sacs that provide cushioning).

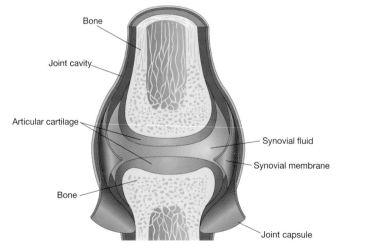

Figure 3.28: Typical synovial joint.

Name _____

Instructor _____

1. The type of tissue characterized by a close arrangement of cells to form protective sheets or secretory clumps is

   a. epithelial tissue
   b. muscle tissue
   c. connective tissue
   d. nervous tissue

2. The tissue that performs a major role in producing body movement, and includes specialized cells that are long, cylindrical, and multinucleate is

   a. dense regular connective tissue
   b. nervous tissue
   c. skeletal muscle tissue
   d. cardiac muscle tissue

3. A tissue that is dominated by thick collagen fibers that extend mostly parallel, allowing little space for cells and ground substance, is known as

   a. dense regular connective tissue
   b. areolar tissue
   c. skeletal muscle tissue
   d. stratified squamous epithelium

4. The tissue that is specialized to store energy, provide insulation, and provide some protection is

   a. compact bone tissue
   b. PSCC epithelium
   c. adipose tissue
   d. dense irregular connective tissue

5. You may observe areolar tissue by viewing the _____.

   a. dermis of the skin
   b. subcutaneous layer
   c. tendons attached to muscle
   d. interior of a bone

6. When viewing a microscope slide that has been prepared with the common H&E stain, you can identify collagen fibers by their _____ color.

   a. red
   b. pink
   c. purple
   d. blue

7. _____ is a protective tissue lining the esophagus with multiple layers of cells.

   a. simple cuboidal epithelium
   b. PSCC epithelium
   c. stratified squamous epithelium
   d. simple columnar epithelium

8. You will be able to identify cilia by observing a prepared slide of the _____.

   a. trachea
   b. urinary bladder
   c. skin
   d. wall of the heart

9. The cells that are specialized for communication by way of electrochemical signals form what tissue?

   a. epithelial tissue
   b. muscle tissue
   c. nervous tissue
   d. connective tissue

10. The cell type that produces proteins and most molecules of the ground substance in cartilage are known as

    a. chondroblasts   c. osteocytes

    b. fibroblasts   d. adipocytes

11. Why do you suppose simple squamous epithelium is suitable for allowing diffusion to occur through it?

12. Other than kidney tubules, where would you find simple cuboidal epithelium?

13. To what function do you think the microvilli contribute?

14. What is the primary functin of stratified epithelium?

15. As a form of stratified epithelium, identify the primary function of transitional epithelium:

16. What function is provided by the goblet cells?

17. What function is provided by the cilia?

18. What function is performed by the fibroblasts?

19. Loose connective tissue often contains white blood cells. Why?

20. What three functions are provided by adipose tissue?

21. How would you distinguish a reticular cell from an adipose cell?

22. Do you think tendons and ligaments can readily repair themselves? Why or why not?

23. What produces the collagen fibers in dense irregular connective tissue?

24. What property is provided by the elastic fibers in elastic connective tissue?

25. Where is hyaline cartilage found in the body?

26. How does a chondroblast differ from a chondrocyte?

27. How can you distinguish the microscopic view of hyaline cartilage from fibrocartilage?

28. How can you distinguish elastic cartilage from the other types of cartilage microscopically?

29. What cells produce the collagen and inorganic salts of bone matrix?

30. How do osteocytes obtain nourishment to survive?

31. With what body system must skeletal muscle tissue be associated in order for it to perform its primary function?

32. How can you distinguish cardiac muscle tissue from skeletal muscle tissue microscopically?

33. What is the function of cardiac muscle tissue?

34. How can you microscopically distinguish smooth muscle tissue from skeletal muscle tissue and cardiac muscle tissue?

35. What is the function of smooth muscle tissue?

36. How can you distinguish between neurons and neuroglia under the microscope?

37. What function is performed by neurons?

APPLYING YOUR NEW KNOWLEDGE

1. Collagen diseases are a group of human diseases in which the production of collagen throughout the body becomes impaired. Some examples of collagen diseases include systemic lupus erythematosus (SLE or lupus), rickets, and osteogenesis imperfecta. Explain why these diseases often affect the entire body.

2. A sarcoma is an aggressive form of cancer that arises from connective tissue. It spreads quickly to other parts of the body. Explain why cancer cells are able to spread to other parts of the body by way of connective tissues.

CHAPTER 4

INTEGUMENTARY SYSTEM

The **integumentary system** consists of the integument, or skin, and includes numerous accessory organs embedded within the skin, such as nails, hair, hair follicles, and glands. The main function of skin is **protection**. It protects the body from mechanical injury (bumps and cuts) by cushioning and insulating the underlying body tissues. Skin establishes a continuous physical barrier that protects underlying tissues from fluid loss, UV radiation, and invasion by microorganisms that could cause disease. The acid mantle, or slightly acidic coating on the skin, assists in fighting microorganisms. The capillary network of the skin helps regulate heat loss from the body surface. The skin is involved in other functions such as excretion in which urea, salts and water are lost through the pores as sweat, and metabolism when vitamin D is synthesized and certain drugs and hormones are activated and inactivated. Finally, the skin contains a variety of sensory organs that allow you to feel various types of sensations. In this chapter, you will learn the structures of the integumentary system, and examine some physiological functions.

The laboratory exercises in this unit correlate to Chapter 5 in your textbook and to the following BIO 231 course objective:

1. Compare the physiology and anatomy of the major components of the integumentary system.

ANATOMY OF THE SKIN

The skin covers your body to protect it from the outside environment and it helps your body maintain homeostasis. Structurally, it consists of two distinct layers that are bound tightly together. The outer, superficial layer is called the **epidermis** (epi- = on top + dermis = skin) which is made of epithelial cells. The inner, deep layer is called the **dermis** and it is made of connective tissue. An undulating border helps cement the epidermis and the dermis together. The layers are distinct and excessive rubbing on the epidermis can cause the two layers to cleanly separate, resulting in a common **blister.** The tissue beneath the dermis is a subcutaneous layer known as the **hypodermis** (hypo- = under, below), or superficial fascia. The hypodermis is not a part of the skin, but instead is a loose configuration of fat and areolar tissue that attaches the skin to the underlying muscles.

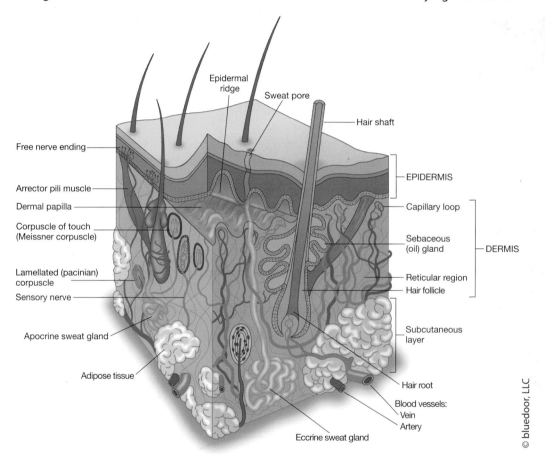

© bluedoor, LLC

Figure 4.1: Skin, human.

Exercise 4.1: Skin Anatomy

Study the anatomy of the skin by reading through the following text and comparing the descriptions with models and charts of the skin in your lab.

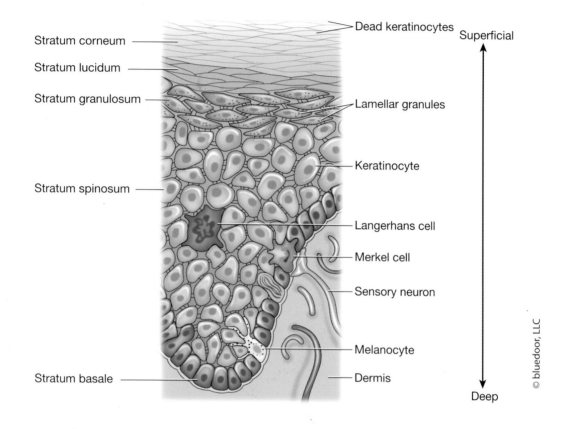

Figure 4.2: Epidermis, human.

Exercise 4.2: Thick and Thin Skin under the Microscope

Thick skin is found where there is an unusually large amount of skin abrasion, such as the palms and the soles. As you might expect, the stratum corneum of this skin is very thick, sometimes with more than 100 layers of flattened, dead cells. Hair and hair follicles are usually not present in thick skin. On the other hand, **thin skin** contains a relatively thin stratum corneum, hair, and hair follicles. In this exercise, you will use the microscope and prepared slides to compare thick skin and thin skin.

1. Obtain a prepared slide of thin skin. Examine the slide specimen under scanning power, then under low power.

2. Compare your specimen with **Figure 4.3** under low power. Identify the stratum corneum, stratum basale, epidermis, papillary region of the dermis, and reticular region of the dermis.

3. Determine how many layers of cells make up the stratum corneum by doing a quick count.

4. Obtain a prepared slide of thick skin from the palm or sole. Examine the slide specimen under scanning power, then under low power.

5. Compare your specimen with **Figure 4.4** under low power. Identify stratum corneum, epidermis, papillary region of dermis, and reticular region of dermis.

6. Return slides to appropriate slide tray.

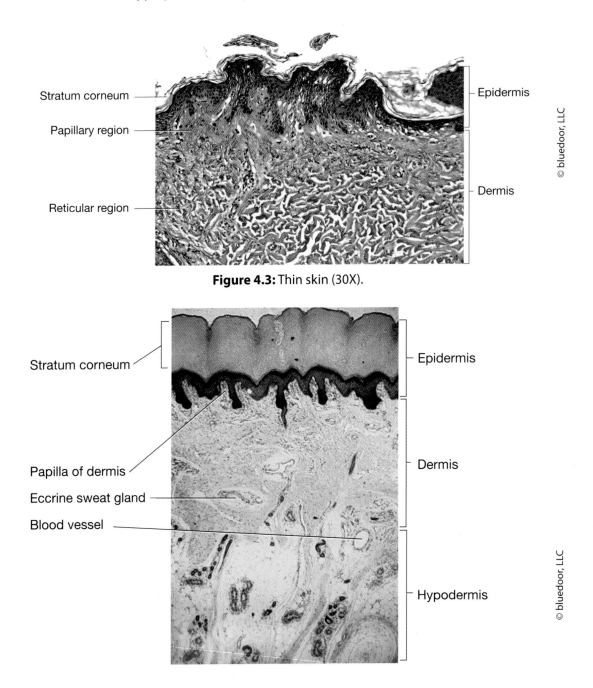

Figure 4.3: Thin skin (30X).

Figure 4.4: Skin from the palm (30X).

Exercise 4.3: Differentiating Sebaceous and Sudoriferous Glands Microscopically

1. Obtain a thin skin with hairs slide or obtain scalp slide and a sudiferous gland slide to differentiate sebaceous and sudoriferous glands.

2. Sebaceous glands are usually found associated with a hair follicle and appear like a clump of epithelial cells. Use **Figure 4.5** as a reference.

3. Sudoriferous glands are not associated with hair follicles and contain a duct that reaches the surface of the skin. On a slide, these glands appear like coiled tubes of single layers of epithelial cells that have been cut in cross section. Use **Figure 4.6** as a reference.

4. Return slides to appropriate slide tray.

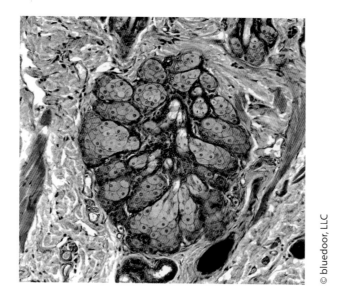

© bluedoor, LLC

Figure 4.5: Microscopic view of cutaneous glands - Sebaceous gland.

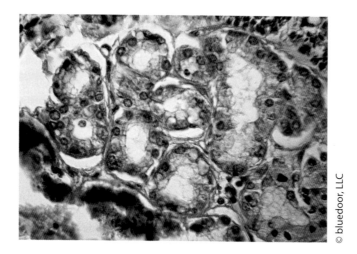

© bluedoor, LLC

Figure 4.6: Microscopic view of cutaneous glands - Eccrine gland.

CHAPTER 4 REVIEW

Name _____

Instructor _____

1. The layer of skin composed of keratinized tissue is the
   - a. dermis
   - b. stratum basale
   - c. epidermis
   - d. hypodermis

2. The part of the epidermis characterized by cells that are flat and filled with tiny granules in the cytoplasm is the
   - a. stratum basale
   - b. stratum corneum
   - c. stratum granulosum
   - d. stratum spinosum

3. The cell layer of the skin containing mitotically active cells is the
   - a. stratum basale
   - b. stratum corneum
   - c. stratum granulosum
   - d. stratum spinosum

4. Thick skin is more adapted for abrasion than thin skin because
   - a. it is more vascular
   - b. the stratum corneum is much thicker
   - c. it contains hair follicles
   - d. it has a thicker stratum basale

5. The part of the dermis that is composed of areolar tissue is the
   - a. reticular region
   - b. hypodermis
   - c. papillary region
   - d. stratum dermis

6. You should be able to observe the hair bulb of a hair in the
   - a. stratum corneum
   - b. papillary region of the dermis
   - c. reticular region of the dermis
   - d. all of the above

7. Hair follicles are composed of
   - a. collagen fibers
   - b. epithelial cells from the dermis
   - c. epithelial cells from the epidermis
   - d. hair roots

8. In most cases, sebaceous glands empty their product
   - a. directly onto the skin surface
   - b. into a hair follicle
   - c. into a long, twisting duct
   - d. into the shaft of a hair

9. Eccrine sweat glands are found in skin covering all of these areas of the body except the
   _____.
   - a. palms of the hand
   - b. lips
   - c. axillary region
   - d. cervical region

10. Apocrine sweat glands are mainly located in the

    a. skin of the forehead   c. armpits and external genitals

    b. palms of the hands   d. visceral organs

11. Approximately how many layers of cells form the stratum corneum in thin skin?

12. List at least three differences between thick skin and thin skin. _____

_____

13. Between thin and thick skin, which is more adapted to abrasion and why?

_____

14. Complete the labeling in the figure below.

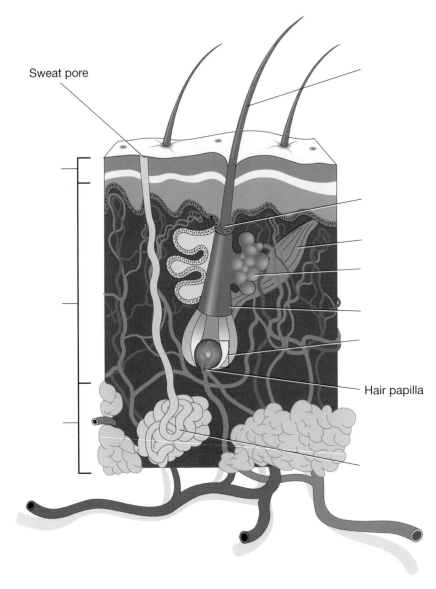

Sweat pore

Hair papilla

APPLYING YOUR NEW KNOWLEDGE

1. The three types of skin cancer are squamous cell carcinoma, basal cell carcinoma, and melanoma, each usually resulting from mutations in the cells. The terminology of each cancer type signifies that cancer's cell of origin, e.g. squamous cell carcinoma arises from cell in the superficial layer of the epidermis (most commonly the stratum granulosum). Based on this information, identify where a basal cell carcinoma arises, and where a melanoma arises.

2. It has been well documented that the three skin cancers described in the preceding question can be caused by damaging exposure to ultraviolet light. Describe the role of the skin in helping to prevent this damage, and also what behaviors you can employ to further prevent skin cancer.

CHAPTER 5

MUSCLE PHYSIOLOGY

The muscular system provides the mechanism for moving the bones, enabling the body to make complex movements. It also generates heat, which is a byproduct of the energy used during muscle contraction. It is composed of more than 500 muscles, each of which is an organ with several types of tissues. The most abundant tissue is skeletal muscle tissue, but a muscle also contains loose connective tissue, dense connective tissue, blood vessels, and nerves, all of which are integrated to achieve the primary function of a muscle: contraction. The process of muscle contraction is a fascinating sequence of cellular events that begins with a stimulus and ends with a shortening in the length of the muscle.

The laboratory exercises in this unit correlate to Chapter 10 in your textbook and to the following BIO 231 course objectives:

1. Compare energy sources used for muscle contraction.
2. Analyze the events of muscle contraction and relaxation.

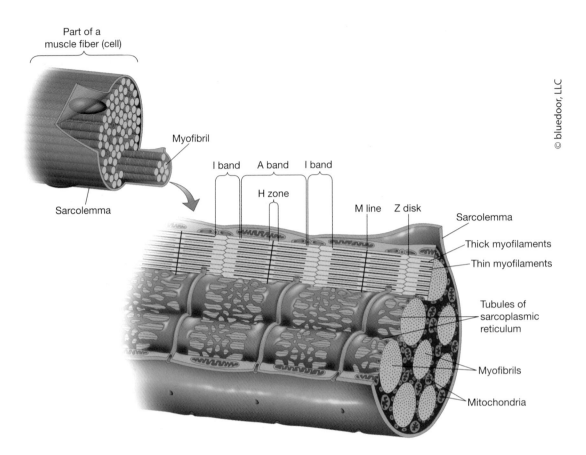

Part of a
muscle fiber (cell)

Myofibril

Sarcolemma

I band   A band   I band

H zone

M line   Z disk

Sarcolemma

Thick myofilaments

Thin myofilaments

Tubules of
sarcoplasmic
reticulum

Myofibrils

Mitochondria

© bluedoor, LLC

Figure 5.1: Cell structure. A portion of a single muscle cell is presented to reveal
the sarcoplasmic reticulum and myofibrils.

MUSCLE ORGANIZATION

Thousands of muscle fibers are bundled together with layers of connective tissue to form a single
muscle (**Figure 8.4**). There are three distinct layers of connective tissue associated with a muscle.
Enclosing each individual muscle fiber is a thin sheet of areolar connective tissue, known as the
endomysium (*endo-* = within + *mysium* = pertaining to muscle). Groups of fibers are surrounded by a
thicker, tougher sheet of connective tissue called the **perimysium** (*peri-* = around), forming a muscle
bundle or **fascicle**. Numerous fascicles are bound together by a collagenous, dense connective tissue
covering called the **epimysium** (*epi-* = on top), which envelops the whole muscle. The epimysium
converges at the terminal end of skeletal muscle tissue, narrowing to form a band of dense regular
connective tissue called a **tendon**. You may know that a tendon forms a firm attachment for the
muscle to the periosteum of a bone. In the previous chapter, you learned that a tendon may connect
to a moveable bone to establish the insertion, or to a stationary bone to establish the origin. A very
wide tendon is called an **aponeurosis**. The epimysia from numerous muscles blend together to form
the **deep fascia**, which binds muscles into functional groups.

The connective tissue coverings provide cohesiveness to muscle, binding the fibers into a single,
functional unit. By way of tendons, they also provide a firm attachment to bone. In addition, blood
vessels and nerves travel through the connective tissue coverings.

MUSCLE PHYSIOLOGY

You have learned that the primary function of the muscular system is the production of movement, which occurs as a result of muscle contraction. In this section, you will learn the basics of how this function occurs and perform laboratory exercises that will examine the process of muscle physiology.

Cellular Events of Muscle Contraction

The contraction of skeletal muscle fibers consists of three events: electrical excitation of the muscle cell, coupling of excitation and contraction, and sliding of the myofilaments within the muscle cell to result in a reduction of cell length.

Muscle fibers
Axon terminals
Motor neuron

© bluedoor, LLC

Figure 5.2: Photomicrograph of the neuromuscular junction. A motor unit with three neuromuscular junctions is visible in this high power image (400X).

Electrical excitation is an event that begins at the neuromuscular junction. When acetylcholine contacts receptors on the motor end plate, the sarcolemma becomes temporarily permeable to sodium ions, which rush into the muscle cell. The sudden influx of sodium ions changes the membrane charge, causing the cell interior to become less negatively charged. This event is called **depolarization**. As the sarcolemma momentarily changes its polarity, sodium ions rush into the cell along the cell's length to produce a depolarization wave. During this change, the sarcolemma becomes impermeable to sodium ions and permeable to potassium ions. As a result, the potassium ions leak out of the cell, restoring the resting potential. This event is called **repolarization**, which occurs in a wave that follows the depolarization wave along the sarcolemma. The rapid depolarization and repolarization that propagates along the membrane is called the **action potential**.

The coupling of excitation and contraction is an event that is triggered by the arrival of the action potential at the sarcoplasmic reticulum (SR) within the muscle cell. The action potential causes a change in permeability of the SR membrane to calcium ions (stored in the SR). The leakage of calcium ions leads to the binding of calcium to the thin myofilaments, causing a structural change that allows the myosin cross bridges to bind chemically to the thin (actin) myofilaments.

During the third event of contraction, myosin will use ATP, if available, to shift in position, producing the "power stroke" movement that shifts the position of the thin myofilaments. ATP will then be used to break the chemical bond between the cross bridges and thin myofilaments, enabling the process to be repeated. A third role of ATP is to provide energy to enzymes that carry calcium ions back into the sarcoplasmic reticulum. The result of the numerous power strokes is a sliding of the thin myofilaments toward the center of the sarcomere. The shifting of the thin myofilaments shortens the length of the sarcomere. When the sarcomeres of the muscle fiber shorten simultaneously, the muscle fiber shortens in length.

Exercise 5.1: Muscle Fiber Contraction

In this observational exercise, you will review the influence of ATP on responsive muscle. You are part of OCC's Undergraduate Research Group. You have been asked to determine what solutions or combination of solutions will cause the psoas major muscle of a rabbit to contract. The findings of your study will be used in future laboratory experiments. The materials and procedure are listed below. Be prepared to answer questions at the end of your experiment that relate to your experiment.

Materials: *Teasing needles, 6 microscope slides, 1 petri dish, a dropper vial with ATP, a dropper bottle with a salt solution, a dropper bottle with ATP plus salt solution, a dropper bottle with glycerol, small bundle of glycerinated rabbit muscle, compound microscope, dissecting microscope.*

1. Obtain a teasing needle, a clean microscope slide and coverslip, a petri dish with glycerol, and small portion of a glycerinated prepared muscle.

2. Place the muscle tissue into the petri dish with glycerol.

3. Using teasing needles, separate the fibers from the clump of muscle tissue. Your goal is to isolate single muscle fibers for observation, so use care and patience when teasing apart the tissue. Do not use your fingers to separate the fibers, and try to avoid breaking the fibers.

4. When you have isolated a single strand, transfer it onto a clean microscope slide with the teasing needles. Use a compound microscope to observe the muscle fibers under low power; then switch to high power. Observe the striations of the muscle fiber, and the fiber's overall appearance in the relaxed state.

    What produces the striations?_____

5. Extract two fibers from the petri dish, and place each on a different clean microscope slide. Carefully arrange them as straight and parallel to one another as possible. With a metric ruler, measure the length of each fiber in millimeters, and record your measurements in **Data Table 5.1**.

6. You are about to saturate the muscle fibers with salt solution. Predict what you will observe once you saturate the fibers for thirty seconds.

7. Saturate the two fibers on the slide with several drops of the salt solution. Using a dissecting microscope, observe the fibers for 30 seconds, and notice any changes in their length and/or diameter. Measure each fiber again and record the new length in the data table. Calculate the percentage change, if any, in each fiber using the formula below:

$$\frac{\text{Beginning length - Ending length}}{\text{Beginning length}} \quad X \quad 100 = \%$$

8. Extract two more fibers from the petri dish, and place each on a different clean microscope slide. Carefully arrange them as straight and parallel to one another as possible. With a metric ruler, measure the length of each fiber in millimeters, and record your measurements in the data table.

9. You are about to saturate the muscle fibers with ATP solution. Predict what you will observe once you saturate the fibers for thirty seconds.

10. Saturate the two fibers on the slide with several drops of the ATP solution only. Using a dissecting microscope, observe the fibers for 30 seconds, and notice any changes in their length and/or diameter. Measure each fiber again and record the new length in the data table. Calculate the percentage change, if any, in each fiber using the formula above and record your answer in the data table.

11. Extract two more fibers from the petri dish, and place each on a different clean microscope slide. Carefully arrange them as straight and parallel to one another as possible. With a metric ruler, measure the length of each fiber in millimeters, and record your measurements in the data table.

12. You are about to saturate the muscle fibers with ATP plus salt solution. Predict what you will observe once you saturate the fibers for thirty seconds.

13. Saturate the two fibers on the slide with several drops of the ATP plus salt solution. Using a dissecting microscope, observe the fibers for 30 seconds, and notice any changes in their length and/or diameter. Measure each fiber again, and record the new length in the data table. Calculate the percentage change, if any, in each fiber using the formula above and record your answer in the data table.

14. Clean-up: Used microscope slides can be disposed of in glass container. Plastic petri dishes can be disposed of in the garbage. Used utensils can be returned to the green trays for cleaning.

Data Table 5.1: Muscle Fiber Contraction

Solution	Fiber #	Beginning Length	Ending Length	Percentage of Change
Salt Solution	Fiber #1			
	Fiber #2			
ATP Solution	Fiber #1			
	Fiber #2			
ATP Plus Salt Solution	Fiber #1			
	Fiber #2			

Graph your results; use the graph paper below.

What can you report back to your undergraduate research advisor about the influence of ATP and salts on muscle tissue? Explain your reasoning. _____

_____

_____

Exercise 5.2: Isotonic and Isometric Contractions

You will compare isotonic and isometric contractions using your own muscles in this observational exercise.

1. Perform an isotonic contraction: position your lab stool within 1 foot of your lab countertop, and sit down. Place your textbook on the lab countertop near the counter edge, and extend one arm to touch the book. Extend with more force to push the book away from you. While doing so, use your other hand to feel the muscles tense in the upper arm and shoulder of the working limb.

2. Perform an isometric contraction: position your lab stool within 1 foot of your lab countertop, and sit down. Push against the edge of the immoveable countertop, but be careful to avoid pushing too hard to unbalance your stool. While you are pushing, use your other hand to feel the muscles tense in the upper arm and shoulder of the working limb.

3. Describe the difference between the isotonic contraction and the isometric contraction:

   _____

   _____

   Based on your experience in the lab, which generated more tension? _____

4. Predict which type of muscle contraction, isotonic or isometric, will induce fatigue more rapidly. Explain your reasoning. _____

   _____

Exercise 5.3: Muscle Fatigue

Working in groups of four, complete the following exercise, and answer the corresponding questions. One student in your group will play the role of a physical therapy assistant (PTA), and the other three group members will play the roles of patients A, B, and C.

You are a physical therapy assistant (PTA) for Oakton Hospital's Rehabilitation Center. Today, you have been assigned three patients. For each patient you will have to test various muscles or muscle groups for rate of fatigue. Upon completion of your testing you will be responsible for developing exercises that will condition the muscles you tested.

Patient A

1. Patient A: Have patient stand in correct anatomical position. Patient should flex the left upper limb at the shoulder joint. Place a 5 lb weight in the patient's left hand. The patient should not grasp the weight. Record the length of time the patient can hold the weight without discomfort or pain and/or without visible shaking of muscles due to fatigue. Record the results in the table that follows.

2. Allow your patient to rest for 1 minute. Repeat the process. Record the results.

3. Allow your patient to rest for 1 minute. Repeat the process. Record the results.

Patient/Trial	Length of Time until Fatigue
Patient A/Trial 1	
Patient A/Trial 2	
Patient A/Trial 3	

4. List the major muscles and their respective actions involved in Patient #A's task. Observe the cadavers as necessary to assist you in this identification process.

5. Determine one exercise for each group of muscles your patient can do at home to condition these muscles.

Patient B

1. Patient B: Have patient stand in correct anatomical position. Patient should slightly flex lower limb at hip joint (do not flex knee joint), just enough to raise foot off of floor. Balance a 5 lb weight on the patient's foot. Record the length of time the patient can hold the weight without discomfort or pain and/or without visible shaking of muscles due to fatigue. Record the results in the table that follows.

2. Allow your patient to rest for 1 minute. Repeat the process. Record the results.

3. Allow your patient to rest for 1 minute. Repeat the process. Record the results.

Patient/Trial	Length of Time until Fatigue
Patient B/Trial 1	
Patient B/Trial 2	
Patient B/Trial 3	

4. List the major muscles and their respective actions involved in Patient B's task. Observe the cadavers as necessary to assist you in this identification process.

5. Determine one exercise for each group of muscles your patient can do at home to condition these muscles.

Patient C

1. Patient C: Have patient stand in correct anatomical position against a bare wall. Patient should flex hips and knee joints to make a sitting position against the wall. Record the length of time the patient can hold position without discomfort or pain and/or without visible shaking of muscles due to fatigue (not due to increased muscle tension). Record the results in the table that follows.

2. Allow your patient to rest for 1 minute. Repeat the process. Record the results.

3. Allow your patient to rest for 1 minute. Repeat the process. Record the results.

Patient/Trial	Length of Time until Fatigue
Patient C/Trial 1	
Patient C/Trial 2	
Patient C/Trial 3	

4. List the major muscles and their respective actions involved in Patient C's task. Observe the cadavers as necessary to assist you in this identification process.

5. Determine one exercise for each group of muscles your patient can do at home to condition these muscles.

Final Questions for Exercise 5.3

1. Considering muscle physiology, what might account for the change in time until muscle fatigue sets in with each subsequent patient trial? _____

   _____

2. Predict how muscle conditioning and muscle deconditioning would change length of time until muscle fatigue. _____

   _____

   _____

   _____

CHAPTER 5 REVIEW

Name _____

Instructor _____

1. Muscle cells are distinct from other cells of the body, mainly because their interior is filled with

   a. water

   b. cytosol

   c. myofibrils

   d. membranous organelles

2. The functional subunit of each muscle cell is called the

   a. myofibril

   b. sarcoplasmic reticulum

   c. sarcomere

   d. muscle fiber

3. Thick myofilaments are a prominent part of the muscle fiber structure. They are composed of

   a. actin

   b. myosin

   c. actin, troponin, and tropomyosin

   d. sarcomeres

4. The connective tissue layer that surrounds individual muscle fibers is known as the

   a. epimysium

   b. endomysium

   c. sarcolemma

   d. perimysium

5. The space between a synaptic end bulb and a motor end plate through which acetylcholine must diffuse is known as a

   a. neuromuscular junction

   b. synaptic vesicle

   c. synaptic cleft

   d. sarcolemma junction

6. The sudden influx of sodium ions into a muscle cell causes a change in membrane polarity, which is known as

   a. depolarization

   b. action potential

   c. repolarization

   d. contraction

7. ATP is a required component for muscle contraction. Its role is to

   a. provide the power stroke

   b. uncouple thin myofilaments and cross bridges

   c. power the removal of calcium ions

   d. all of the above

8. In the absence of ATP, you would expect the percentage of change in a muscle fiber length after receiving a stimulus to be

   a. 5 mm

   b. 10 volts

   c. zero

   d. 20%

APPLYING YOUR NEW KNOWLEDGE

1. An injury to the tendon can cause local swelling and pain to the tendon and is referred to as tendonitis. When the body of the muscle is damaged by stretching it beyond its normal range, the injury is called a muscle strain. In a severe injury, the tendon may become detached, usually at its union with the bone. Why do you suppose the detachment of a tendon is more likely to occur at the bone than at the muscle?

2. Certain toxins are capable of blocking the Ach receptors within a motor end plate. Explain the health consequences of a heavy exposure to this type of toxin.

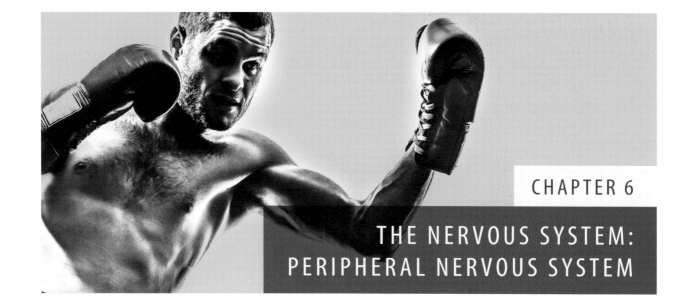

CHAPTER 6

THE NERVOUS SYSTEM: PERIPHERAL NERVOUS SYSTEM

The nervous system is organized into two primary parts: the **central nervous system (CNS)**, consisting of the brain and spinal cord, and the **peripheral nervous system (PNS)**. (PNS, i.e., nerve tissue beyond the CNS or outside the dorsal cavities.) The CNS receives information from sensory receptors, coordinates and integrates the information, and initiates and transmits a response. The PNS consists of nerves and ganglia, which channel impulses to and from the CNS. Sensory, or afferent, nerves carry impulses from sensory receptors to the CNS, and motor, or efferent, nerves transmit impulses from the CNS to effector organs such as neurons, muscles, and glands.

The exercises in this chapter will help you to understand the basic anatomy and some of the physiology of the spinal cord, the spinal nerves and the cranial nerves.

The laboratory exercises in this unit correlate to Chapter 13 in your textbook and to the following BIO 231 course objectives:

1. Compare reflex pathways.
2. Differentiate between cranial nerves by location and function.

SOMATIC REFLEXES

A reflex is a function performed by the nervous system that triggers a rapid response for the purpose of maintaining homeostasis. In most cases, a reflex provides protection from an event in order to avoid or minimize injury to the body. A reflex resulting in contraction of skeletal muscle is known as a **somatic reflex**; a reflex involving the contraction of cardiac muscle, smooth muscle, or glands is called an **autonomic (visceral) reflex**; a reflex involving spinal nerves is called a **spinal reflex**, while a reflex mediated by cranial nerves is known as a **cranial reflex**.

The simplest form of a reflex is called a **reflex arc**, which involves a simple pathway that contains five components (**Figure 6.1**):

3. **Sensory receptor:** Detecting a stimulus, the sensory receptor triggers an action potential or impulse (provided that stimulus is strong enough).

4. **Sensory neuron:** The action potential conducted by the sensory neuron to the CNS, which terminates at a synapse in the spinal cord (in a spinal reflex) or in the brain stem (in a cranial reflex).

5. **Integration center:** The action potential is passed to one or more neurons in the spinal cord or brain stem by way of synapses in order to form this center.

6. **Motor neuron:** From the integration center, the action potential, transmitted along the motor neuron, is conducted to the effector.

7. **Effector:** The action potential activates the effector to perform work, the effector being skeletal muscle (as in a somatic reflex), or cardiac muscle, smooth muscle or gland (as in a visceral reflex).

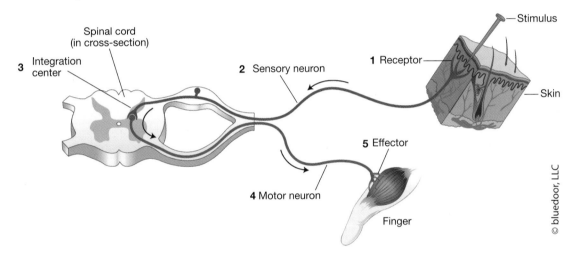

Figure 6.1: A simple reflex arc. The numbers correspond to the sequences in the text.

The simple reflex arc just described consists of only two neurons, and is called monosynaptic. However, most reflexes of the body are more complex, involving more neurons and more than one level of the spinal cord; they are called polysynaptic (**Figure 6.2**). Testing reflexes in a patient is a simple procedure that can inform (or give clues to) the health professional of possible damage or disease involving peripheral nerves, the spinal cord, or brain.

Exercise 6.1: Testing the Integrity of the Nervous System

You are a neurologist for Oakton Hospital. Your schedule today consists of four new patients (your lab partners). Three of the patients have been referred to you by their family physician for different reasons and you will assess the fourth patient in the emergency room. You will need to assess each patient's reflexes to complete one aspect of the neurological exam. Refer to the following grading scale to rate your patients' responses.

Table 6.1: Grading scale to rate patients' responses.

Grade	Description of Reflex Response	What does this mean?
0	No response; always considered abnormal	Hyporeflexia
1+	Response apparent but slight	May or may not be normal (see discussion below)
2+	Normal, rapid response	All components of reflex arc are intact
3+	Response is very rapid	May or may not be normal (see discussion below)
4+	Clonic reflex response; always abnormal	Hyperreflexia

Hyporeflexia is a diminished or absent reflex response that typically involves one or more components of a reflex arc. If the reflex response is absent and there are evident sensory losses, this typically indicates the afferent nerve component or dorsal horns are involved. If the reflex response is absent and also associated with muscle atrophy or paralysis, this typically indicates a problem with the efferent pathway. In order to determine if a patient truly has a diminished reflex response, a grade of 1+ for example, it is important to know how that patient has always responded to that reflex stimulus. A grade 1+ is considered normal if the patient's response has always been 1+.

Hyperreflexia is a hyperactive response or a response that results in clonic reflexes. Clonic reflexes are responses to stimuli that result in rapid and repetitive relaxation and contraction of muscles. Hyperreflexia is typically a result of a lesion of upper motor neurons (UMNs). UMNs are neurons located above the area of the reflex pathway. UMNs are integral to regulating the function of the lower motor neurons of the reflex pathway. Keep in mind, a reflex response with a grade of 3+ may be considered normal. Just like a grade of 1+, if a person has always had a response of 3+, then a grade of 3+ is normal for that person.

Patient A: Patient A suffers from type I diabetes and has been referred to you to determine if peripheral neuropathy has developed as a result of diabetes. You will conduct four somatic reflex tests. Use the grading scale above to rate your patient. Record Patient A's results in the **Table 6.2**.

1. Patellar reflex. When the patellar tendon is stretched, the response is a rapid extension of the leg at the knee. The reflex arc is illustrated in **Figure 6.2**. Perform the following test on a volunteer subject from your lab:

   a. Direct the subject to sit on a lab stool with one leg dangling free of contact from the stool or the floor. Find the patella and tibial tuberosity of the subject by palpation. The patellar ligament is located between the two. Check to make sure you have found the patellar ligament by having the subject tense the quadriceps muscles (tension without movement is called isometrics).

   b. Gently, but firmly, tap the patellar ligament with the tapered end of a rubber-tipped reflex hammer. If no reflex occurs, try the patellar ligament of the opposite leg. What nerve carried the motor impulse? _____

c. Repeat the test, except this time distract your subject's attention by asking her or him to describe their most recent meal in detail while you tap the patellar ligament. Is the motor response stronger or weaker than without the distraction? _____

_____ If there is any difference, suggest an explanation.

_____

2. **Biceps reflex.** The biceps reflex is the rapid contraction of the biceps brachii muscle in response to a sudden stretch of the biceps tendon.

    a. Direct the subject to stand upright with one arm completely relaxed and hanging at the side. Ask the subject to flex the biceps brachii isometrically (tense it without producing movement). With the biceps flexed, palpate the biceps tendon, which you will find in the antecubital fossa.

    b. Place your thumb over the tendon, and ask the subject to relax the arm once again. Gently but firmly, tap your thumb with the tapered end of the reflex hammer. If you observe no reflex, repeat on the opposite arm.

    What nerve carries the sensory neurons involved in this reflex?

    _____

    What nerve (s) carries the motor neurons in this reflex?

    _____

3. **Achilles reflex.** The Achilles reflex examines the first two sacral segments of the spinal cord. It results in plantar flexion when the calcaneous (Achilles) tendon is stretched.

    a. Direct the subject to remove both shoes and stand upright with one foot on the floor and the knee of the other leg on a chair, with the sole of the foot free of the chair's edge.

    b. Direct the subject to dorsiflex the foot slightly to increase the tension on the gastrocnemius muscle while relaxing the rest of the body. Tap the calcaneal tendon with the tapered end of the reflex hammer. What is the result?

    _____

4. **Plantar reflex.** The plantar reflex is a common clinical test that examines the pyramidal tract of the brain, in addition to the peripheral nerves that are associated with the reflex arc. In adults, this reflex normally causes the toes to flex and move closer together. If the toes extend (flare apart with dorsiflexion of the first toe), this reflex is then abnormal and is referred to as the Babinski sign or reflex and damage to the pyramidal tract may be its cause. In newborn infants, the Babinski sign is normal during the first 18 months of age (due to incomplete myelination of the nervous system).

    a. Direct the subject to remove a shoe and lie on a cot or the laboratory bench with both knees slightly bent and the thighs rotated to make the lateral side of the foot contact with the horizontal surface.

    b. Use the handle end of the reflex hammer to firmly draw an imaginary curved line down the lateral side of the exposed sole, extending from the heel to the base of the big toe. What is the subject's response?

    _____

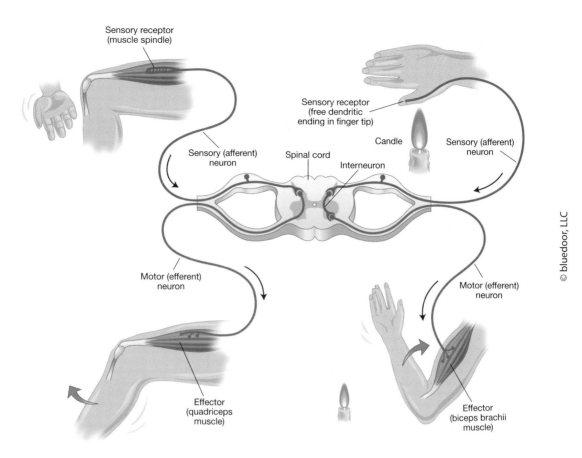

Figure 6.2: Monosynaptic and polysynaptic reflexes.
(a) Monosynaptic reflex uses two neurons, such as the patellar reflex.
(b) A polysynaptic reflex uses more than two neurons, such as the biceps reflex.

Table 6.2: Patient A Reflex Responses

Somatic Reflex	Grade
Patellar Reflex	
Biceps Reflex	
Achilles Reflex	
Plantar Reflex	

Patient A Discussion:

1. If your patient (your lab partner) did truly suffer from diabetes and associated peripheral neuropathy, predict what type of reflex response you would expect to witness.

Patient B: Patient B suffers from hypothyroidism. She has been referred to you by her endocrinologist. The endocrinologist would like a neurological exam to ensure there are not any underlying neurological conditions. Conduct the same four somatic reflexes you conducted on Patient A. Use the same grading scale to rate your patient. Record Patient B's results in **Table 6.3**.

Table 6.3: Patient B Reflex Responses

Somatic Reflex	Grade
Patellar Reflex	
Biceps Reflex	
Achilles Reflex	
Plantar Reflex	

Patient B Discussion:

1. If your patient (your lab partner) did truly suffer from hypothyroidism, predict what type of reflex response you would expect to witness.

Patient C: Patient C has been referred to you by the patient's family physician. The patient takes Prozac, an SSRI, to treat depression. The family physician suspects the patient suffers from serotonin syndrome. Serotonin syndrome results from overstimulation of serotonin receptors in nuclei of the midbrain and medulla oblongata. Conduct the same four somatic reflexes you conducted on Patient A. Use the same grading scale to rate your patient. Record Patient C's results in **Table 6.4**.

Table 6.4: Patient C Reflex Responses

Somatic Reflex	Grade
Patellar Reflex	
Biceps Reflex	
Achilles Reflex	
Plantar Reflex	

Patient C Discussion:

1. If your patient (your lab partner) did truly suffer from serotonin syndrome, predict what type of reflex response you would expect to witness.

Patient D: You are suddenly called to the ER to conduct a neurological exam on a 65 y/o male that was brought in a few hours earlier. He has just been diagnosed with pneumonia. He suffered an ischemic stroke one month earlier. Conduct the same four somatic reflexes you conducted on Patient A. Use the same grading scale to rate your patient. Record Patient D's results in **Table 6.5**.

Table 6.5: Patient D Reflex Responses

Somatic Reflex	Grade
Patellar Reflex	
Biceps Reflex	
Achilles Reflex	
Plantar Reflex	

Patient D Discussion:

1. If your patient (your lab partner) did truly suffer from an ischemic stroke, predict what type of reflex response you would expect to witness.

Exercise 6.2: Two-Point Discrimination Test

The somato-sensory system allows us to detect many sensations, modalities, such as pain, temperature, touch, vibration, pressure and proprioception (body position). The brain's perception of the modality of "touch" can include different types of "touch sensation". Light touch, tickle and itch are gross or crude sensations, conducted through the antero-lateral (spinothalamic) ascending spinal tract. On the other hand, touch modalities such as stimulus or point localization, two-point discrimination, vibration (and even conscious positional sense) require precise integration and often interpretation and "knowledge" (gnosis) and these afferent signals are conducted along the dorsal columns of the spinal cord.

The ability to perform two-point discrimination basically allows a person to detect whether touching the skin at two points is perceived as actually two separate points or only as a single point. We can measure this by applying calipers or compass to the skin, gradually widening the space between the caliper points and "see at what width" the person can discern or perceive two separate points. This simple "two point discrimination test" is widely employed clinically to assess hand sensation following trauma, surgery, grafting and re-implantation

You are a registered nurse working in the neurology department at Oakton Hospital. Dr. X asked you to conduct a two-point discrimination test on two returning patients (student partners). Before your patients arrive you quickly review how a two-point discrimination exam is conducted.

Dermatome Chart

Showing the relationship between spinal nerve levels and sensory sectors in the body.

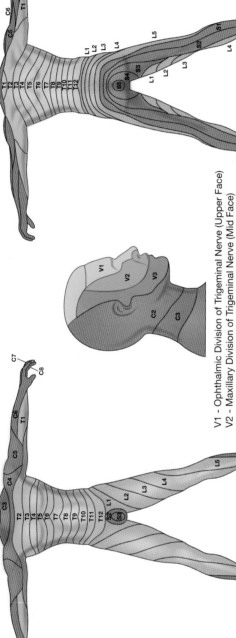

V1 - Ophthalmic Division of Trigeminal Nerve (Upper Face)
V2 - Maxillary Division of Trigeminal Nerve (Mid Face)
V3 - Mandibular Division of Trigeminal Nerve (Lower Face)

Dermatome sectors on all diagrams are approximate, due to the way sensory nerves naturally overlap in the body

Upper Quarter Screen

C2 - Occipital Protuberance
C3 - Supraclavicular Fossa
C4 - Acromioclavicular Joint
C6 - Thumb
C7 - Middle Finger
C8 - Little Finger
T1 - Medial Antecubital Fossa
T2 - Apices of Axillae

Lower Quarter Screen

L1 - Upper Anterior Thigh
L2 - Mid Anterior Thigh
L3 - Medial Femoral Condyle
L4 - Medial Calf
L5 - Dorsum 3rd MTP Joint
S1 - Lateral Heel
S2 - Popliteal Fossa
S3 - Ischial Tuberosity
S5 - Perianal Area

Figure 6.3: Dermatome Chart.

Materials: calipers and metric rulers

1. Test each body region listed below for two-point discrimination.
   - Thumb: Anterior surface
   - Thumb: Posterior surface
   - Palmar surface
   - Hand: Posterior surface
   - Arm: Lateral surface
   - Arm: Medial surface

2. At each body region, start by placing closed calipers on skin surface. Slowly increase the distance between the caliper needles until patient can sense two distinct points of contact.

Prior to conducting this test on your incoming patients, work with your lab partners to make some predictions.

1. Predict which of the body regions will have the greatest two-point discrimination distance? See body regions listed above. Explain your reasoning.

2. Predict which of the body regions will have the shortest two-point discrimination distance? See body regions listed above. Explain your reasoning.

Patient A: Patient A is a 21 y/o returning for a follow up visit after a serious motor vehicle accident that resulted in multiple bone fractures of the humerus, first metacarpal and second metacarpal in his right upper limb. The fractures did cause nerve damage. Conduct the two-point discrimination test to determine the patient's current two-point discrimination threshold.

Table 6.6:

Patient A	Body Surface	Two-Point Distance (cm)	Spinal Nerve(s) Being Assessed *
	Thumb: Anterior Surface		
	Thumb: Posterior Surface		
	Palmar Surface		
	Hand: Posterior Surface		
	Arm: Lateral Surface		
	Arm: Medial Surface		

* Refer to **Figure 6.3** to view the spinal nerves associated with various body regions.

* **Patient A Discussion**: If your lab partner actually suffered from a series of fractures and associated nerve damage of the upper limb, would you expect the two point discrimation distance to increase or decrease as a result of the injuries? Explain your reasoning.

Patient B: Patient B is a 5 y/o recovering from skin grafts on her hands after suffering from third degree burns. Conduct the two-point discrimination test to determine the patient's current two-point discrimination threshold.

Table 6.7:

Patient B	Body Surface	Two-Point Distance (cm)	Spinal Nerve(s) Being Assessed *
	Thumb: Anterior Surface		
	Thumb: Posterior Surface		
	Palmar Surface		
	Hand: Posterior Surface		
	Arm: Lateral Surface		
	Arm: Medial Surface		

* Refer to **Figure 6.3** to view the spinal nerves associated with various body regions.

* **Patient B Discussion**: If your lab partner actually suffered from third degree burns and associated skin grafts, would you expect the two point discrimation distance to increase or decrease as a result of the injuries? Explain your reasoning.

Exercise 6.3: Cranial Nerve Testing: Testing the Integrity of the Nervous System

You are a medical student attending Oakton Hospital. Today you are working in the clinic conducting cranial nerve examinations. For the purpose of this exercise, you will conduct a cranial nerve examination on one patient (a lab partner). For each test conducted, determine what cranial nerve(s) you are testing.

Test 1:

Test 1 Procedures	Patient's Results
Assess pupil size, shape and symmetry.	
Assess pupillary light reaction. Conduct this test in an area with reduced light. Standing directly in front of your patient and using a pen light, start by shining the light at the patient's right ear. Pass the light across the right eye. Observe the pupil size in the right eye as well as the left eye.	
Assess patient's ability to follow your finger with his/her eye without moving his/her head. Move the finger in an 'H' pattern to assess upward, downward and lateral movements.	
Assess convergence: examiner should move finger towards patient's nose.	

Predict which cranial nerve(s) was/were being examined in Test 1.

Test 2:

Test 2 Procedures	Patient's Results
Conduct Weber's Test. Place a vibrating tuning fork on top of patient's head. Ask the patient on which side is the sound heard better.	
Conduct Rinne's Test. Place a vibrating tuning fork on patient's mastoid process. Ask patient to indicate when they stop hearing it. Immediately move the tuning fork next to the ear. Ask patient if they hear sound and if so, which tuning fork placement was louder – on the mastoid process (sensorineural) or next to the ear (air conduction). Air conduction should be better than bone conduction.	

Predict which cranial nerve(s) was/were being examined in Test 2.

Test 3:

Test 3 Procedures	Patient's Results
Assess patient's speech. Ask patient to speak. Is voice hoarse or nasally? Is voice soft, weak and/or 'breathy'?	
Assess patient's ability to swallow. Ask patient to swallow.	
Assess soft palate movement. Ask patient to open mouth and say 'ahhh'.	

Predict which cranial nerve(s) was/were being examined in Test 3.

Test 4:

Test 4 Procedures	Patient's Results
Assess facial symmetry.	
Assess facial expression muscles: • Ask patient to raise eyebrows. Examine forehead wrinkling and look for loss of wrinkling and asymmetry. • Ask patient to shut eyes. Examine symmetry. • Ask patient to smile. Note nasolabial folds and examine symmetry. • Ask patient to show teeth. Examine symmetry of facial muscles.	

Predict which cranial nerve(s) was/were being examined in Test 4.

Test 5:

Test 5 Procedures	Patient's Results
Give the patient a visual acuity test using an eye chart.	

Predict which cranial nerve(s) was/were being examined in Test 5.

Test 6:

Test 6 Procedures	Patient's Results
Assess blink reflex. Ask patient to place a transparency in front of their face for protection. Once their face is protected, throw a cotton ball at their eyes. Watch both eyes for a blinking response.	
Assess sensory responses of facial skin. Using sterile dull and sharp probes, touch probes to forehead, cheek and jaw. Ask patient to report if sensation is sharp or dull	
Assess jaw jerk reflex. Place your finger on tip of patient's jaw. Using the reflex hammer, tap your finger lightly. You will witness one of two things: (1) nothing, which usually happens, or, (2) a slight closure of the jaw.	

Predict which cranial nerve(s) was/were being examined in Test 6.

Test 7:

Test 7 Procedures	Patient's Results
Assess symmetry of trapezius. Standing behind the patient, examine the superior surface of the trapezius and sternocleidomastoid muscles. Look for atrophy or asymmetry.	
Assess shoulder and neck muscle movements. Ask patient to shrug shoulders and examine symmetry. Ask patient to rotate head and examine symmetry.	

Predict which cranial nerve(s) was/were being examined in Test 7.

Test 8:

Test 8 Procedures	Patient's Results
Ask patient to stick out tongue. Examine position of tongue for any deviation to the right or left.	

Predict which cranial nerve(s) was/were being examined in Test 8.

Consider the following patients and determine what cranial nerve(s) have been compromised by the patients' disease/disorder. Explain your reasoning for each of your determinations.

Patient A: Patient complains of brief episodes of burning facial pain. Episodes last for 10-15 seconds at a time and occur about 5-6 times/day. Pain radiates from lateral surface of cheek to lower eyelid, nose, upper teeth and upper lip. Pain is not relieved by over the counter nonsteroidal anti-inflammatories.

1. What cranial nerve(s) is/are affected?

2. Explain your reasoning.

Patient B: Patient B is an elderly male that suffers from diabetes mellitus, Type II, and high blood pressure. Patient B complains of a sudden paralysis of his left eye. He cannot elevate, depress or adduct his left eye. Upon visual examination, it is obvious that Patient B's left eye is 'pointed' down and laterally (out) and that his left upper eyelid droops.

1. What cranial nerve(s) is/are affected?

2. Explain your reasoning.

Patient C: Patient C recently underwent a lymph node biopsy in the neck. After the surgical procedure, the patient complained of shoulder pain and difficulty lifting and rotating shoulders. Upon visual examination, you notice atrophy of the trapezius muscle.

1. What cranial nerve(s) is/are affected?

2. Explain your reasoning.

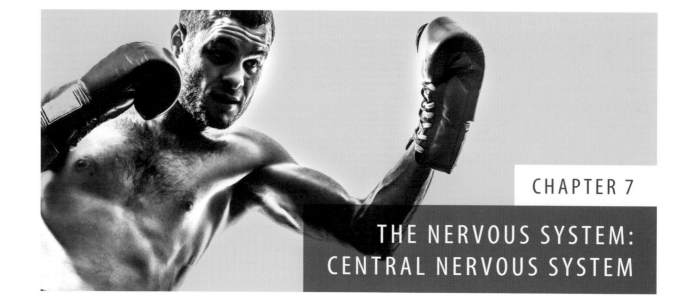

CHAPTER 7

THE NERVOUS SYSTEM: CENTRAL NERVOUS SYSTEM

The nervous system is a complex part of the body that has been studied extensively, yet there is still much more to learn. The system is composed of the brain, spinal cord, nerves, and ganglia. Together, these important organs enable you to sense the world around you, integrate this information to form thoughts and memories, and control body movements as well as many internal functions. The rapid communication between different parts of the body this system achieves serves one central purpose: to maintain homeostasis.

The laboratory exercises in this unit correlate to Chapters 12 and 14 in your textbook and to the following BIO 232 course objectives:

1. Identify principle brain structures and explain their main functions.

2. Compare the ways in which various structures of the CNS communicate with one another.

Sheep Brain Dissection

The brain of a sheep shares many similarities with the human brain. You will notice the same structures that you have studied in the human, and many of them have similar features such as cerebral convolutions and gray and white matter distribution. However, the sheep brain is considerably smaller, particularly the cerebrum.

Exercise 7.1: Sheep Brain Dissection

You will dissect a preserved sheep brain in this exercise and compare its gross anatomy with the human brain. The preserved tissues provide an excellent dissection experience because the chemical preservative dries out the tissue, making it firmer and easier to dissect. By contrast, the unpreserved brain is gelatinous, and disintegrates during a dissection. *Safety precaution: Wear disposable gloves, eye protection, and a lab coat when handling preserved materials for protection against the chemical preservative, which is an irritant. Also, wash your hands thoroughly after the exercise, and follow your instructor's directions for cleaning your work area and saving or disposing of the specimen.*

3. Obtain a sheep brain specimen, rinse it with water to remove excess preservative, and place it on a dissecting tray.

4. With the brain on its ventral side, examine the dorsal surface (**Figure 7.1** and **7.2**). If the tough **dura mater** is present, identify it, then carefully remove it. As you do so, identify the **falx cerebri** extending into the **longitudinal fissure** and the **tentorium cerebelli** extending into the **transverse fissure**. Deep to the dura mater is the **arachnoid**, which is a web-like connection between the dura and the deep meningeal layer, the **pia mater**. Notice that the pia mater adheres to the surface of the brain and conforms to its contours, and contains blood vessels.

5. With the brain still on its ventral side, observe the dorsal surface and identify the **cerebrum**, **cerebellum**, and **spinal cord** (**Figure 7.1** and **7.2**). Now turn the brain on its dorsal side, and identify the **brain stem** (the **pons** and **medulla oblongata** are externally visible) (**Figure 7.3**). Also identify the **olfactory bulbs** of CN I, the **olfactory tracts**, the **optic chiasma**, the **cerebral peduncles**, and the **mammillary bodies**. During removal of the brain from the cranial cavity, it is common for the pituitary gland to be torn from the infundibulum due to its tight confinement within the sella turcica of the skull. Therefore, although the pituitary gland may not be present, identify the **infundibulum** that should remain. Compare the appearance of these structures with those of the human brain.

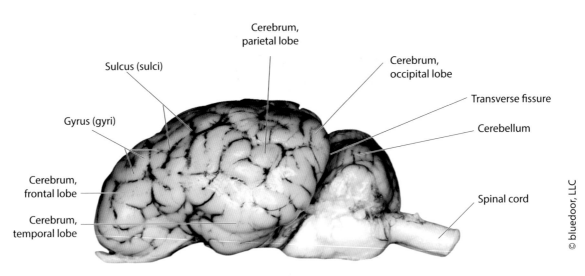

Figure 7.1: Brain, lateral view, sheep.

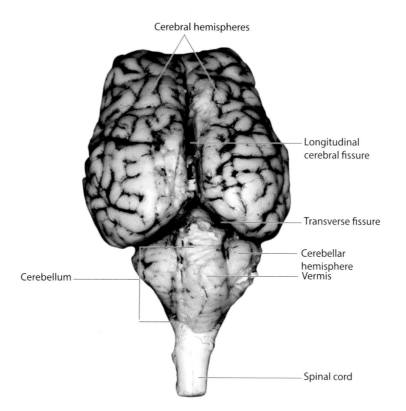

Figure 7.2: Brain, superior view, sheep.

Cerebral hemispheres

Longitudinal cerebral fissure

Transverse fissure

Cerebellar hemisphere

Vermis

Cerebellum

Spinal cord

© bluedoor, LLC

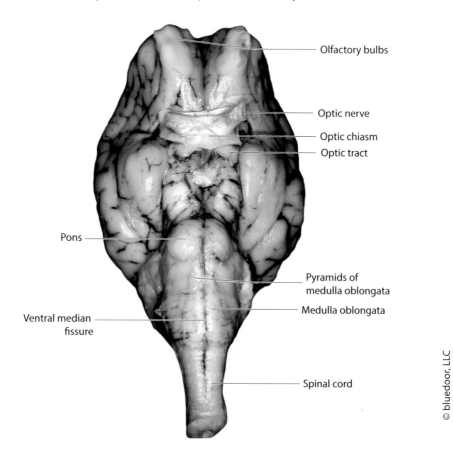

Figure 7.3: Brain, inferior view, sheep.

Olfactory bulbs

Optic nerve

Optic chiasm

Optic tract

Pons

Pyramids of medulla oblongata

Medulla oblongata

Ventral median fissure

Spinal cord

© bluedoor, LLC

6. Lift the brain from the dissecting tray and, as shown in **Figure 7.4**, separate the cerebrum from the cerebellum by carefully pulling the cerebellum downward to open the transverse fissure and reveal the **superior colliculi** and **inferior colliculi** of the midbrain. You should also be able to observe the **pineal gland** (body). If the superior colliculi were damaged, what functions would become impaired?

_____

_____

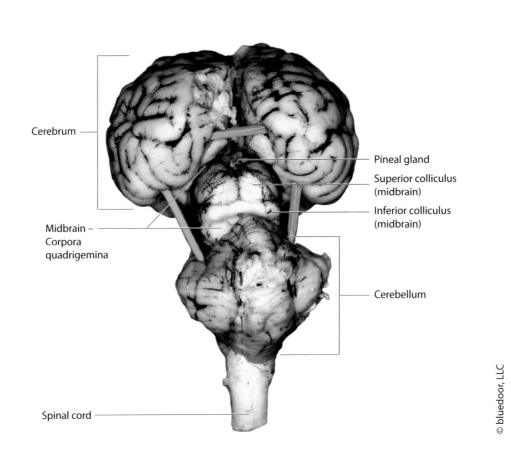

Cerebrum

Pineal gland

Superior colliculus (midbrain)

Inferior colliculus (midbrain)

Midbrain – Corpora quadrigemina

Cerebellum

Spinal cord

Figure 7.4: Dorsal midbrain structures, sheep.

7. Place the brain on its ventral side in the dissecting tray. With a large scalpel, press the blade into the longitudinal fissure and press down to cut through the entire brain. Slide the blade from rostral (front of the sheep brain) to caudal (back of the sheep brain to the spinal cord) in a single stroke to slice the brain cleanly into right and left halves. Observe the sliced interior of the brain as shown in **Figure 7.5**, and identify the **cerebrum, corpus callosum, fornix, transverse fissure, septum pellucidum, cerebellum, optic chiasma, corpora quadrigemina, pons**, and **medulla oblongata**. What part of the brain is the corpora quadrigemina a component of? _____

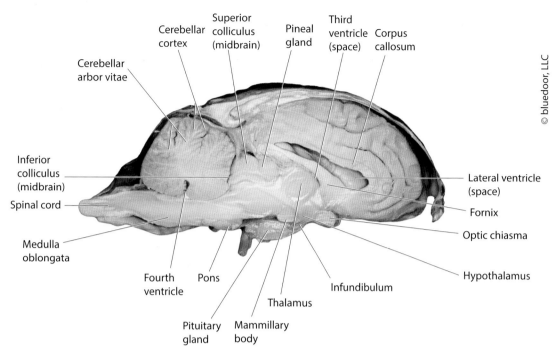

Figure 7.5: Brain, midsagittal view, sheep.

8. Continue your study of the sectioned brain by using a probe to examine the ventricles (**lateral ventricle, third ventricle, fourth ventricle**) and interconnecting channels (**interventricular foramen, cerebral aqueduct**) carefully. Also, distinguish between white matter and gray matter in the cerebrum and the cerebellum. What is the white matter of the cerebellum called? _____What are the clusters of gray matter embedded within the white matter of the cerebrum called? _____

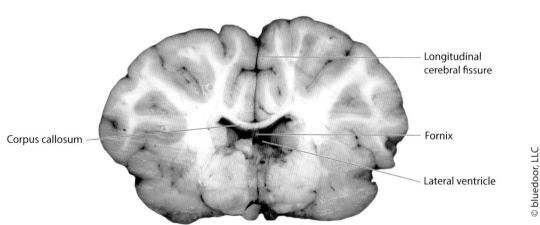

Figure 7.6: Cerebrum, coronal view, sheep.

9. Clean-up: Wrap brains in moist paper towels and store in plastic bags. Make sure to put your name on bag and place in tray with course instructor's name. Any tissue not needed can be thrown in garbage. Clean and dry all dissecting tools. Rinse dissecting trays, dry and reline with new paper towel.

CHAPTER REVIEW

Name _____

Instructor _____

1. The primary motor area of the brain:

   a. is located in the cerebellum   c. initiates motor impulses

   b. receives most sensory impulses   d. is the main integration center

2. The corpus callosum, projection fibers, and basal ganglia are all:

   a. part of the cerebrum   c. located in the left hemisphere

   b. composed of gray matter   d. active in managing emotions

3. In order to observe convolutions in the sheep brain, you must first remove the:

   a. cerebral cortex   c. dura mater

   b. pia mater   d. cranial nerves

APPLYING YOUR NEW KNOWLEDGE

1. Neural tissue of the CNS is unable to replace itself through mitosis and regeneration. Because of this, the neural tissue is very vulnerable to damage from the pressure of adjacent expanding tumors. This tumor pressure on the normal tissue results in death of the neurons and often tragic disability to the patient. A meningioma is a tumor that arises from cells within one of the meningeal layers surrounding the brain and spinal cord. Explain the possible symptoms that a meningioma arising from the pia mater at the superior sagittal sinus may cause.

2. Multiple sclerosis is an autoimmune disease affecting the CNS, in which the microglia appear to attack and erode the myelin sheath produced by oligodendrocytes. The result of this erosion is a gradual loss of nerve function in the localized areas involved by the disease process. Explain the loss of function that would result after an attack in the cerebral cortex of the temporal lobe.

3. A patient experiences a sudden impairment of speech, called aphasia, caused by a ruptured blood vessel in the brain, referred to as a cerebrovascular accident (CVA), or hemorrhagic stroke. Identify the cerebral lobe in which this occurred, and the cranial nerves that are affected.

   Discuss the differences between fluent and non-fluent aphasia.

The senses are important extensions of the nervous system that enable us to detect changes in the environment. The changes, or stimuli, provide us with information about the world around us and within us. When our senses detect these stimuli and send them to the brain for interpretation, we are able to make decisions about how to react.

The senses include touch, temperature, pain, vision, and hearing, as well as others. In each case, a **sensory receptor** detects a stimulus. The sensory receptor is a microscopic component that contains dendrites to sensory neurons, which generate an action potential when a stimulus of a particular type is sufficiently strong. Some sensory receptors are widely distributed within the skin, muscles, and walls of visceral organs, where they detect the **general senses**, which include touch, pressure, temperature, pain, stretch, and vibration. Other sensory receptors are isolated in large, complex sensory organs, where they detect the **special senses**, including vision, hearing, equilibrium, smell, and taste.

The laboratory exercises in this unit correlate to Chapter 15 in your textbook and address the following BIO 232 course objective:

1. Correlate the anatomy of the eye, ear, and olfactory system to the functional pathways for these senses.

SPECIAL SENSES

The special senses, including vision, hearing and equilibrium, taste, and smell, enable you to examine the external environment for the broad purpose of maintaining homeostasis. In each special sense, the sensory receptors are dendrites of sensory neurons associated with other tissues that form an organ. Thus, the eye is the organ of vision, the ear is the organ of hearing and equilibrium, the taste buds are the organs of taste, and the nose is the organ of smell. In this part of the chapter, you will learn about each special sensory organ by performing a series of learning exercises.

Exercise 8.1: Dissection of the Cow Eye

The cow eye is the common preserved specimen for studying the eye, although the sheep eye may also be used; either specimen provides an excellent learning experience for understanding the structure of the human eye. _Safety precaution: Use disposable gloves when you dissect the preserved cow or sheep eye, and dispose of all material as directed by your lab instructor._

2.   Obtain a dissection tray, a dissection kit that includes a scalpel, pair of scissors, and blunt probe, and disposable gloves. Put the gloves on, obtain a preserved eye, rinse it to remove excess preservative, then place it on the dissecting tray.

3.   In most specimens, the posterior surface of the eye is obstructed with fat tissue; carefully cut away this tissue to expose the optic nerve. Identify the external eye structures that are now visible: **sclera**, **cornea**, **optic nerve**, and **extrinsic eye muscles** (**Figures 8.1a** and **8.1b**). The cornea is opaque in most specimens due to the preservative.

4.   With the scalpel, slice into the eye to create an opening about 1/4 inch posterior to the corneal and scleral union. As you do so, take care to avoid squeezing the eye to prevent fluid from squirting out.

5.   Once you have penetrated the eye, use your scissors to cut the eye into an anterior half and a posterior half **_by cutting around the circumference of the eyeball parallel to the corneal edge_**. As you cut, take care to keep the **vitreous humor** in the posterior half and the **lens** in the anterior half, and identify them (**Figure 8.1c**). Similar to the cornea, the lens looses its transparency due to exposure to the preservative.

6.   Remove the lens carefully by cutting through the **suspensory ligaments**, which attach the lens to the ciliary muscle. Examine the anterior half of the eye, and identify the **ciliary body**, the **iris**, and the **pupil** (**Figure 8.1c**).

7.   Turn your attention to the posterior half of the eye, and carefully scoop out the vitreous humor. Identify the **retina** as the thin, off-white or tan membrane on the inside posterior wall of the eye **Figure 8.1c**). In many cases, the preservative causes it to detach from the underlying **choroid**, which is a darker color due to its pigments. The choroid of the cow or sheep has an iridescent surface called the tapetum lucidum, which reflects the light within the eye, but which is absent in the human choroid.

8.   Clean-up: Put dissected eye in a plastic bag. Make sure to add name to bag and place in tray with instructor's name. Any unwanted tissue can be disposed of in the garbage. Clean and dry all dissection tools. Rinse and dry dissecting tray. Reline tray with new paper towels.

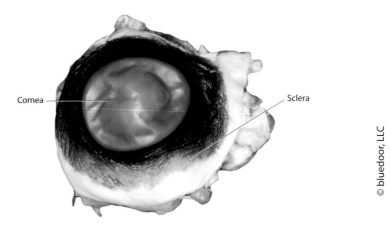

Cornea — Sclera

© bluedoor, LLC

Figure 8.1a: The cow eye, anterior view.

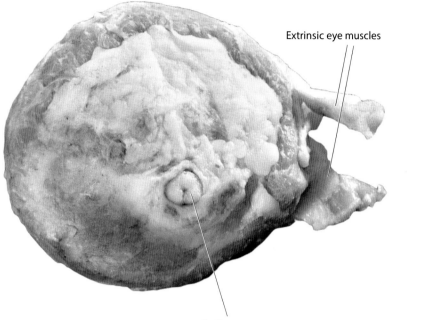

Extrinsic eye muscles

Optic nerve

© bluedoor, LLC

Figure 8.1b: The cow eye, posterior view

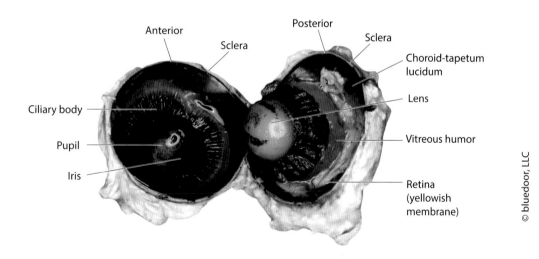

Anterior

Sclera

Posterior

Sclera

Choroid-tapetum
lucidum

Ciliary body

Lens

Pupil

Vitreous humor

Iris

Retina
(yellowish
membrane)

© bluedoor, LLC

Figure 8.1c: Internal structures of eye, cow.

PHYSIOLOGY OF THE EYE

The parts of the eye that you have just studied work in unison to direct light into the interior of the eye and onto the retina, where the rods and cones respond by generating action potentials. The action potentials pass to the bipolar cells, then to the ganglion cells, whose axons exit the eye via the optic nerve (CN II). As the optic nerves converge at the optic chiasm, nerve fibers along the medial aspects of each nerve criss-cross to the opposite side through the chiasm ("a crossing") and continue along the optic tracts. The optic tracts will eventually synapse with neurons in the lateral geniculate nucleus. From there, neurons extend to the visual cortex in the occipital lobe of the cerebrum to synapse with cortical cells, where visual interpretation occurs.

Exercise 8.2: Visual Acuity

You will perform a simple test for visual acuity, or sharpness of vision, by the use of a Snellen eye chart in the lab.

1. Testing for **distance visual acuity** requires the use of a Snellen eye chart, which will be provided by your instructor. The chart consists of letters of various sizes on a white background. The distance at which the emmetropic eye can read a line of letters of a particular size is printed at the end of each line.

2. Instruct your subject to stand 20 feet from the Snellen eye chart, and cover one eye with a card or their hand. Ask the subject to read each consecutive line out loud, beginning with the largest letters, and check carefully for accuracy. If the subject wears glasses, direct her or him to read the chart twice: once without corrective lenses and once with them (as a safety precaution, do not remove contact lenses if the subject wears them, simply note that they were worn during the test).

3. Record the number of the line with the smallest letters that can be read correctly. Instruct your subject to cover the opposite eye and repeat the procedure. A reading of 20/20 means that at 20 feet the reading is normal, or emmetropic. A reading of 20/40 indicates that the subject sees at 20 feet what someone with normal vision sees at 40 feet. Therefore, the subject is nearsighted, or _____. A visual acuity of 20/15 indicates that a person can see an object at 20 feet what the emmetropic eye sees at 15 feet. Record your results:

   Visual acuity of right eye without glasses: _____

   Visual acuity of right eye with glasses, if applicable: _____

   Visual acuity of left eye without glasses: _____

   Visual acuity of left eye with glasses, if applicable: _____

4. You will now test for **near visual acuity** by using the Snellen eye card in **Figure 8.2**. Instruct your subject to read the letters in **Figure 8.2** with the face only 12–14 inches (27-35 cm) from the page. Repeat the procedures in steps 2 and 3 above, using the short distance adjustment. Record your results:

   Visual acuity of right eye without glasses: _____

   Visual acuity of right eye with glasses, if applicable: _____

   Visual acuity of left eye without glasses: _____

   Visual acuity of left eye with glasses, if applicable: _____

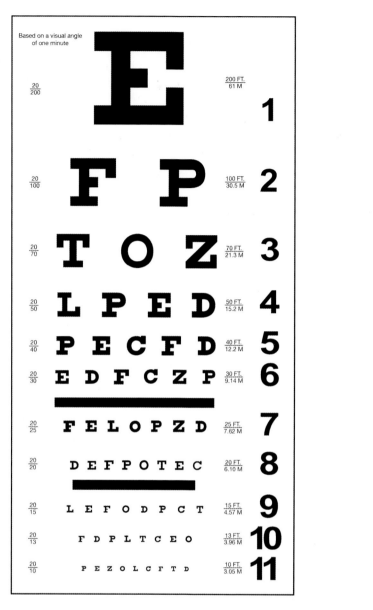

Figure 8.2: Snellen card for testing near visual acuity and near point of accommodation.

Exercise 8.3: Astigmatism

Astigmatism may be tested by the use of a chart, similar to visual acuity. The chart is designed to test for defects in the refractive surface of the lens and the cornea.

1. Using yourself as the subject because this simple test does not require assistance, view the astigmatism chart in **Figure 8.3** first with one eye closed, then the other eye closed. Focus your vision on the center of the chart.

2. If all of the radiating arms appear equal (that is, you can see three lines in each arm and read the numbers with equal success), there is no distortion of refraction. However, if some of the lines are blurred or some arms appear lighter than others, some distortion is present. Is astigmatism present in your right eye?_____ In your left eye? _____. If so and you use corrective lenses, try the test while wearing your glasses.
Do you see an improvement?_____

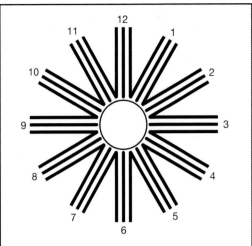

Figure 8.3: Astigmatism chart.

Exercise 8.4: Determining Near Point of Accommodation

The near point of accommodation is a test for measuring the flexibility of the lens, which is influenced mainly by age.

1. Instruct your subject to view the Snellen eye card in **Figure 8.2** within 27 – 35 cm of the face, and cover one eye while reading the letters from the line just above his or her near visual acuity.

2. Slowly move the page closer to the subject's face until the letters become out of focus, then measure and record the distance (in cm) between the subject's face and the Snellen eye card:

    _____

3. Repeat this procedure for the opposite eye, measure, and record: _____.

4. How does this value compare with the normal value of a young adult? _____

    _____

Near Point of Accomodation Normal Values:	
Age	**Near Point of Accomodation (cm)**
10	9
20	10
30	13
40	18
50	53
60	83
70	100

Near Point of Accomodation Class Data Sheet		
Age	**Left Eye (cm)**	**Right Eye (cm)**

5. Record your results in the class data chart.

6. Calculate left and right eye averages for each person in the class.

7. Calculate averages for all students who are the same age.

8. Make a graph of the results with age on the X axis and Near Point averages on the Y axis. Use the graph below. Graphs should include a title, labels, and a key if necessary. Once you complete your graph, answer questions 8 and 9 that immediately follow the graph paper.

9. Discuss what the class results show.

10. How does a person's age impact the near point of accomodation measurement?

Exercise 8.5: The Blind Spot

The blind spot is a small area of the visual field in which vision is not possible, because it corresponds to the optic disc, which lacks photoreceptors. Both rods and cones are absent in the optic disc because it is the location where the axons of ganglion cells converge to form the optic nerve. In this simple exercise, you will find the blind spot in your visual field.

1. Cover one eye and look with the other eye at **Figure 8.4**. Fix your stare slightly to one side of one object in the figure, either the square or the circle.

2. Move the page to within about 10 inches (25 cm) of your face, and slowly bring the page closer to your eye. At a particular distance, the lateral object will disappear from your vision because the image has fallen upon the blind spot in your retina.

Figure 8.4: Blind spot test.

Exercise 8.6: Testing for Color Blindness

Ishihara's color-blindness plates are designed to test for deficiencies in the cones of the retina. There are three cone types:

1. Type 1– primarily absorbs the red wavelengths of visible light
2. Type 2 – primarily absorbs the blue wavelengths of visible light
3. Type 3– primarily absorbs the green wavelengths of visible light.

Nerve impulses reaching the brain from these different cone types are then interpreted as red, blue or green. Interpretation of the intermediate colors of the visible light spectrum is a result of simultaneous excitation of more than one cone type.

1. View the color plates in bright light while holding them about 30 inches (76 cm) away and at right angles to your line of vision. Report to your lab partner your results taking no more than 3 seconds for each decision.
2. Your partner should write down your responses and compare them to the correct answers provided in the color plate book.

Is there any indication that you have some degree of color blindness?

If so, what type?

Exercise 8.7: Testing the Accommodation Pupillary Reflex

Have your partner gaze for approximately 1 minute at a distant object in the lab, but not toward a window or other light source. Observe your partner's pupils and measure the diameter in millimeters. Record below. Then hold some printed material 6-8 inches (15-20 cm) from his/her face and direct him/her to focus on reading the printing. Measure the diameter of his/her pupils and record below.

PUPIL DIAMETER WHEN LOOKING AT A DISTANCE: _____

PUPIL DIAMETER WHEN LOOKING CLOSEUP: _____

Explain the value of this reflex.

Exercise 8.8: Anatomy of the Ear

1. Study models and charts of the ear that are available in the lab. As you do so, identify the following structures:

outer ear	middle ear	tympanic cavity
inner ear	auricle	tympanic membrane
external auditory canal	ceruminous glands	malleus
incus	stapes	oval window
round window	semicircular canals	vestibule
cochlea	cochlear duct	

Return models to storage cabinet or rack.

2. Review the anatomy of the ear by completing the labels in **Figure 8.5**. Using your textbook to assist you, record the missing labels in the blank spaces below:

1. _____   5. _____

2. _____   6. _____

3. _____   7. _____

4. _____   8. _____

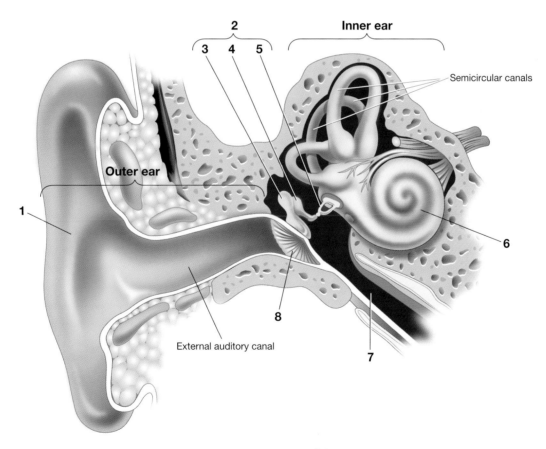

Figure 8.5: Anatomy of the ear exercise.

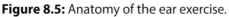

© bluedoor, LLC

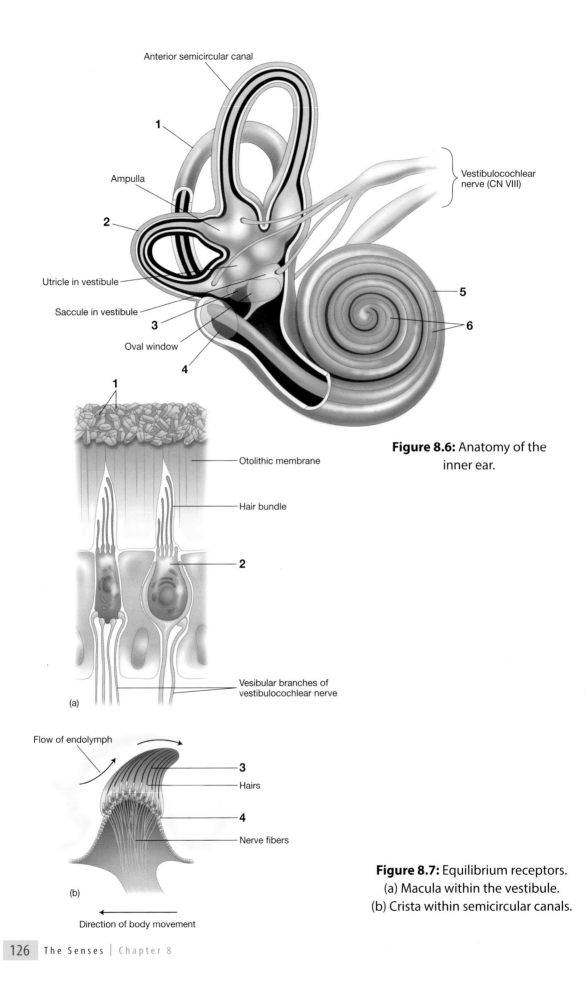

Anterior semicircular canal

1

Ampulla

2

Utricle in vestibule

Saccule in vestibule

3

Oval window

4

Vestibulocochlear
nerve (CN VIII)

5

6

Figure 8.6: Anatomy of the
inner ear.

1

Otolithic membrane

Hair bundle

2

Vesibular branches of
vestibulocochlear nerve

(a)

Flow of endolymph

3

Hairs

4

Nerve fibers

(b)

Direction of body movement

Figure 8.7: Equilibrium receptors.
(a) Macula within the vestibule.
(b) Crista within semicircular canals.

3. Review the anatomy of the inner ear structures by completing the labels in **Figure 8.6**. Using your textbook to assist you, record the missing labels in the blank spaces below:

1. _____   4. _____

2. _____   5. _____

3. _____   6. _____

4. Review the anatomy of the equilibrium receptors of the semicircular canals and the vestibule by completing the labels in **Figure 8.7**. Using your textbook to assist you, record the missing labels in the blank spaces below:

1. _____   3. _____

2. _____   4. _____

Exercise 8.9: Auditory Tests

A loss of hearing may result from a failure to conduct sound waves and vibrations to the inner ear, called **conduction deafness**, or a neurological failure such as damage to the vestibulocochlear nerve (CN VIII), known as **sensorineural deafness**. In this exercise you will perform two common hearing tests. The **Weber test** examines the subject's ability to conduct sound waves. The **Rinne test** examines for the possibility of both conduction deafness and sensorineural deafness.

1. **Weber test**

    1. Obtain a tuning fork and instruct your subject to sit with head erect and face forward.

    2. Strike the tuning fork on the base of your palm and place the handle against the middle of the subject's forehead to test hearing by bone conduction.

    3. Ask the subject if the sound is heard equally in both ears or if one ear hears the sound louder than the other. Circle which of the three possible results have occurred:

        a. Equal loudness in both ears = normal hearing or both ears have equal loss.

        b. Sound is louder in right ear = conduction deafness in right ear or sensorineural deafness in left ear.

        c. Sound is louder in left ear = conduction deafness in left ear or sensorineural deafness in right ear.

2. **Rinne test**

    1. Strike the tuning fork on the base of your palm and place the handle against the subject's right mastoid process. This will test hearing by bone conduction through the temporal bone.

    2. Ask the subject to inform you when the sound can no longer be heard via the mastoid; then quickly move the tuning fork close to the subject's adjacent ear (on the same side as the mastoid process test) and evaluate for any air conduction of sound that may still be detected. Repeat the mastoid and air conduction tests on the other ear.

3. Normally, the subject will continue to hear the tuning fork when it is repositioned next to the ear (air conduction normally is more prolonged compared with bone conduction).
    Circle which of the results are observed:

    a. Air conduction is longer than bone conduction (right ear).

    b. Air conduction is less than bone conduction (right ear).

    c. Air conduction is longer than bone conduction (left ear).

    d. Air conduction is less than bone conduction (left ear).

3. **Auditory Acuity Test**

    Perform the following tests in a quiet area.

    Have your lab partner pack one ear with cotton and sit quietly with eyes closed. Obtain a ticking clock or pocket watch and hold it very close to his or her unpacked ear. Then slowly move it away from the ear until your partner signals that the ticking can no longer be heard. Record the distance in cm at which ticking is audible.

    Right ear: _____   Left ear: _____

4. **Sound Localization**

    Perform the following tests in a quiet area.

    Ask your partner to close both eyes. Hold the pocket watch at an audible distance (about 5-6 inches = 13-15 cm) from his /her ear. Then move the watch to various locations (front, back, sides and above the head). Have your partner locate the position by pointing in each direction.
    Can the sound be localized equally well in all locations?

    If not, how do you explain that?

5. **Application of Hearing Tests:**

    Suppose you are working in the hearing clinic at Oakton Community Hospital. Your job is to perform preliminary hearing tests on patients before they are seen by the attending physician.

    One of the patients is an 80 y/o female:

    Weber test results: Patient reports being able to hear the tuning fork equally well in both ears.

    Rinne test results: Patient reports being able to hear the sound longer when the tuning fork is placed on the mastoid process then when placed near the opening of the left ear. Patient reports being able to hear the sound longer when the tuning fork is placed next to the right ear than when placed on the mastoid process.

    Is this patient exhibiting normal or abnormal results?

    If tests are abnormal, does this patient have symptoms of conduction deafness or sensorineural deafness?

    Would this patient most likely benefit from a hearing aid or a cochlear implant?

    Explain…

Exercise 8.10: Equilibrium Tests

The equilibrium receptors in the semicircular canals and vestibule enable the body to maintain body position and coordination, and to perceive body movement. Injury or illness to the receptors can result in a loss of body coordination, dizziness, and confusion of circular motion (vertigo). The **Romberg test** is a very simple test for static equilibrium, and the **Barany test** evaluates the function of the receptors that monitor dynamic equilibrium.

1. **Romberg test**

   a. Have your partner stand with his/her back to the blackboard

   b. Draw one line parallel to each side of your partner's body. He/she should stand erect, with feet together, eyes open and staring straight ahead for 2 minutes while you observe any movements. Do you observe any swaying movements? Describe:

   _____

   _____

   c. Have your partner close his/hers eyes and repeat the same test. Record your observations:

   _____

   _____

2. **Barany test**

   a. Choose a subject who does not readily experience nausea with circular motion. Instruct your subject to sit in a rotating chair with eyes closed and head tilted about 30° forward. Identify two students from the lab who are prepared to prevent the subject from a possible fall off of the chair.

   b. Instruct the subject to hold onto the arms of the chair, position the student helpers around the chair, and rotate the chair in one direction for about 10 seconds at a rate of about 2 rotations per second. If the subject begins to experience nausea, stop the test immediately.

   c. Stop the rotation after 10 seconds suddenly, and keep the subject seated in the chair. Look carefully into the subject's eyes immediately, and record the movement of the eyes by circling your observation:

   Lateral eye movement = the cristae in the lateral semicircular canals are stimulated.

   Vertical eye movement = the cristae in the anterior semicircular canals are stimulated.

   Rotational eye movement = the cristae in the posterior semicircular canals are stimulated.

   d. Repeat the test with the subject's head in a tilted position toward one side. Are the eye movements different? _____

3. **Role of Vision in Maintaining Equilibrium**

   To further demonstrate the role of vision in maintaining equilibrium have your lab partner stand erect with their eyes open. Raise the left foot approximately 10-12" off the floor and hold it there for 1 -2 minutes.
   Record observations:

   Repeat the same experiment with the same foot raised, but with the eyes closed.
   Record observations:

CHAPTER REVIEW

Name _____

Instructor _____

1. Shining a light into the eye causes the _____ to reduce the diameter of the pupil in order to reduce the amount light entering the eye.

    a. lens   c. ciliary body
    b. iris   d. cornea

2. The axons from ganglion cells in the retina converge toward the optic disc, which establishes the area of "no vision" referred to as the:

    a. fovea   c. macula lutea
    b. blind spot   d. choroids

3. A reading of 20/40 on the Snellen eye chart indicates that the subject sees at 20 feet what someone with normal vision sees at 40 feet. The condition is called:

    a. emmetropia   c. myopia
    b. hyperopia   d. astigmatism

4. The mechanoreceptors involved in hearing may be found:

    a. within the cochlear duct   c. in the organ of Corti
    b. on top of the basilar membrane   d. all of the above

5. Gustation and olfaction are both detected by:

    a. cutaneous receptors   c. photoreceptors
    b. chemoreceptors   d. receptors on the tongue

APPLYING YOUR NEW KNOWLEDGE

1. Keratoplasty is a corrective surgery of the eye that involves removal of a diseased cornea and replacement with one obtained from a cadaver. The most common reason for corneal replacement is the age-related condition known as cataracts, in which the cornea (or lens in some cases) loses its transparency. Explain why wearing sunglasses outside can result in the reduced need for keratoplasty, and the consequences of excessive exposure to sunlight.

2. Otitis media (OM) is the most common type of ear inflammation among children. Usually caused by a bacterial infection, it often begins as a sore throat or cold. Describe why a bacterial infection is able to spread quickly from the throat to the tympanic cavity. Why do you think the insertion of drainage tubes to remove fluids can save the child from hearing loss?

3. Discuss the causes of near-sightedness and far-sightedness.

4. Discuss the causes of astigmatism.

5. What types of problems could result in conduction deafness?

CHAPTER 9

THE ENDOCRINE SYSTEM

The endocrine system works hand in hand with the nervous system to regulate body functions. Like the nervous system, the endocrine system provides a method of control to keep the body functioning despite changing conditions in the internal environment. In other words, the primary role of the endocrine system is to maintain homeostasis. When the endocrine system becomes deficient due to disease, the result is a homeostatic imbalance that often affects overall health.

The laboratory exercises in this unit correlate to Chapter 16 in your textbook and address the following BIO 232 course objectives:

1. Associate the hormones of the endocrine glands to their actions
2. Compare the mechanisms involved in regulation of hormone secretion

Exercise 9.1: Testing the Effects of Insulin

1. Divide class into teams of four.
2. Each person in a team will be assigned to an experimental group. Record team member's name to respective experimental group as listed in **Table 9.1**.

Experimental Group A (one team member) – no ingestion of liquids during experiment

Experimental Group B (one team member) – ingestion of 8 oz of water during experiment

Experimental Group C (two team members) – ingestion of 8 oz of orange juice during experiment

Table 9.1: Experimental Group Assignments

	Experimental Group A	Experimental Group B	Experimental Group C1	Experimental Group C2
Name:				

3. Once teams have been formed and students are assigned to an experimental group, each student's recent food/drink history must be taken and recorded. Record results below.

Experimental Group A

    a. Have you had anything to eat in the last six hours?   YES   NO

        If yes, how long ago did you ingest something to eat? _____

        If yes, what did you ingest? _____

    b. Have you had anything to drink in the last six hours?   YES   NO

        If yes, how long ago did you ingest something to drink? _____

        If yes, what did you ingest? _____

Experimental Group B

    a. Have you had anything to eat in the last six hours?   YES   NO

        If yes, how long ago did you ingest something to eat? _____

        If yes, what did you ingest? _____

    b. Have you had anything to drink in the last six hours?   YES   NO

        If yes, how long ago did you ingest something to drink? _____

        If yes, what did you ingest? _____

Experimental Group C1

    a. Have you had anything to eat in the last six hours?   YES   NO

        If yes, how long ago did you ingest something to eat? _____

        If yes, what did you ingest? _____

    b. Have you had anything to drink in the last six hours?   YES   NO

        If yes, how long ago did you ingest something to drink? _____

        If yes, what did you ingest? _____

Experimental Group C2

    a. Have you had anything to eat in the last six hours?   YES   NO

        If yes, how long ago did you ingest something to eat? _____

        If yes, what did you ingest? _____

    b. Have you had anything to drink in the last six hours?   YES   NO

        If yes, how long ago did you ingest something to drink? _____

        If yes, what did you ingest? _____

4. Once history is completed, each experimental group should take a baseline blood glucose reading using a glucometer (blood glucose monitoring system). Record results in **Table 9.2**.

Table 9.2: Blood Glucose Levels

Intervals	Experimental Group A	Experimental Group B	Experimental Group C1	Experimental Group C2
Baseline Blood Glucose Level, 0 minutes				
Time of ingestion				
Blood Glucose Level, 15 minutes after ingestion				
Blood Glucose level, 30 minutes after ingestion				
Blood Glucose level, 45 minutes after ingestion				
Blood Glucose level, 60 minutes after ingestion				

5. Make some predictions:

    a. Predict which Experimental Group will have the greatest increase in blood glucose levels during the course of the experiment. Explain your reasoning.

    b. At which time interval after ingestion of the liquid do you expect to see blood glucose levels peak? Explain your reasoning.

6. Once predictions are made, Experimental Groups B and C should ingest their assigned 8 oz of fluid. Time ingestion should be noted in **Table 9.2**.

7. At 15 minutes past the time of ingestion, all experimental subjects should measure their blood glucose levels. Record results and time in **Table 9.2**.

8. At 30 minutes past the time of ingestion, all experimental subjects should measure their blood glucose levels. Record results and time in **Table 9.2**.

9. At 45 minutes past the time of ingestion, all experimental subjects should measure their blood glucose levels. Record results and time in **Table 9.2**.

10. At 60 minutes past the time of ingestion, all experimental subjects should measure their blood glucose levels. Record results and time in **Table 9.2**.

11. After acquiring all of the data, answer the following questions:

    a. Which Experimental Group had the greatest increase in blood glucose levels over the one hour of measurements?

    b. Which Experimental Group had the smallest increase in blood glucose levels over the one hour of measurements?

    c. For the Experimental Group with the greatest increase in blood glucose levels, at what time interval did the blood glucose levels peark?

    d. Were the results you predicted in step #5 similar to the actual results?

       YES   NO

       Could any of the Experimental Group member's food/drink history account for any of the differences between your predictions and the actual results? Explain your reasoning.

12. **Clean-up:** All used glucose strips should be placed in biohazard containers. Clean lab bench surfaces with 10% bleach solution. Return all other materials to green trays for cleaning or throw in garbage if materials are disposable.

e. Explain how a negative feedback loop might affect or influence glucose levels after the peak measurement.

f. If a person had untreated type II diabetes, what would you expect to happen to blood glucose levels at 60 minutes? Throughout each of the intervals? Explain your reasoning: what do you think would happen and why?

CHAPTER REVIEW

1. Which of the following endocrine glands are located within the thoracic cavity?

   a. pancreas
   b. thyroid gland
   c. adrenal glands
   d. thymus

2. Which of the following is composed of nervous tissue?

   a. anterior pituitary
   b. adrenal cortex
   c. pineal gland
   d. posterior pituitary

3. What organ sends signals to the pituitary gland that regulate its secretion activity?

   a. hypothalamus
   b. anterior pituitary
   c. pineal gland
   d. stomach

4. Thyroxine and triiodothyronine are produced by:

   a. parafollicular cells
   b. the parathyroid glands
   c. follicle cells of the thyroid
   d. alpha cells of the pancreas

5. The hormone calcitonin:

   a. is produced by the thyroid gland
   b. reduces calcium levels in the blood
   c. is produced by parafollicular cells
   d. all of the above

6. The part of the pancreas that produces the hormones insulin and glucagon is the:

   a. body of the pancreas only
   b. acini
   c. pancreatic islets
   d. all of the above

7. The hormone that is released into the bloodstream in response to rising levels of glucose is called:

   a. thyroid hormone
   b. insulin
   c. glucagon
   d. cortisol

APPLYING YOUR NEW KNOWLEDGE

1. Diseases of the endocrine system usually are based on an abnormal reduction of a hormone's availability, called hyposecretion or an abnormal increase, called hypersecretion. In the condition "hypothyroidism," the thyroid hormones are below-normal levels, perhaps because of inherited deficiency involving the thyroid physiology, or deficiency in dietary iodine (iodine is necessary for the manufacture of thyroid hormones), or a tumor of the pituitary gland. Advanced stages of hypothyroidism result in the growth (hypertrophy) of the thyroid gland producing large goiters. Using a negative feedback loop, explain how iodine deficiency results in goiters.

2. The anterior pituitary gland influences the function of several endocrine organs, as you have learned. Predict the consequences of a hyperactive anterior pituitary in a young child.

CHAPTER 10

THE CARDIOVASCULAR SYSTEM: BLOOD

Blood is the vital fluid that transports substances necessary for survival, including oxygen, nutrients, enzymes, hormones, and waste materials. Blood circulates within blood vessels and is propelled mainly by the heart. Together, the blood, blood vessels, and heart form the cardiovascular system. Because the lymphatic system is closely associated with blood vessels, it is sometimes combined with the cardiovascular system to form the more encompassing entity known as the circulatory system. Blood is a type of connective tissue, with a fluid ground substance, a sparse protein matrix, and suspended cells.

The blood is a convenient tool for evaluating health. It is easy to withdraw and analyze, and the composition of most healthy people's blood is very similar. In most forms of disease, clues to the type, nature, and cause of the disease can be found from a sample of blood. In the lab exercises presented in this chapter, you will have the opportunity to experience some of the clinical procedures often used to evaluate health by evaluating a sample of blood.

The laboratory exercises in this unit correlate to Chapter 17 in your textbook and address the following BIO 232 course objective:

1. Examine the physiology of blood including blood types and hemostasis

CLINICAL BLOOD TESTS

A clinical blood test is an examination performed on a sample of blood to determine the health status of a patient. Also known as a hematologic test, it is a diagnostic tool that can provide important information on a condition the patient may be experiencing. For example, bacterial infections cause a rise in neutrophils and monocytes, which can be measured with a test known as a differential white blood cell count. Many clinical blood tests are now available, providing health care professionals with a repertoire of data that can be used to help administer treatment. In this section, you will conduct two of the most common clinical blood tests.

Blood Typing

Blood typing is a procedure that identifies the particular type of blood a subject or patient carries and it is necessary in order to determine the compatibility of blood types between individuals. Failure to match blood types properly between recipient and donor prior to a surgical procedure canbe disastrous for the patient–incompatible blood types will result in widespread destruction of red cells. Therefore, blood typing is a routine procedure for blood transfusions, transplantations, and pregnancy planning, and is also useful in genetic mapping and medical research. The most common forms of blood typing are the **ABO system** and the **Rh factor**. Other blood factors, including Kell, Lewis, M, and N, are a consideration limited to patients requiring multiple blood transfusions.

The concept of blood typing is based on the presence of antigenic molecules on the surface of red blood cell membranes (**Figure 14.6**). An **antigen**, or agglutinogen, is a substance that generates an immune reaction, resulting in the production of molecules known as **antibodies** or agglutinins. The antibodies react with the antigens to render them harmless. In the ABO system, there are two types of antigens present on the surface of red blood cell membranes, referred to as A and B (**Figure 14.7**). A person with A antigens has antibodies in the blood that are compatible, that is, they will not attack the A antigens. This type of blood is simply called **type A**. Similarly, blood with B antigens is called **type B**. A third type in the ABO system, **type O**, lacks both A and B antigens, and a fourth type is known as **type AB**, which contains both A and B antigens.

Although type A blood contains antibodies that are compatible with the A antigens, it also contains antibodies that will attack and destroy other antigens, including B antigens. These antibodies are called anti-B antibodies. Thus, a person with type A blood has anti-B antibodies, and a person with Type B blood has anti-A antibodies. A person with type O blood has both types of antibodies. If type A blood were to mix with type B blood, the anti-B antibodies would attack and destroy the B antigens on the red blood cells of the type B blood. Conversely, the anti-A antibodies in type B blood would attack and destroy the A antigens on the red blood cells of the type A blood. The incompatibility reaction between the two types of blood causes the damaged red blood cells to clump together, or **agglutinate**.

In the Rh factor, there is only one type of antigen that may be present on the red blood cell membrane. If the Rh antigen is present, the blood type is called **Rh+**, and if it is not, the blood type is **Rh-**. A person with Rh+ or Rh- blood does not have the Rh+ antibody, as you would find in the ABO system. Instead, the Rh antibody can be produced if there is an exposure to the Rh antigen from Rh+ blood. An exposure can occur during a blood transfusion, by sharing hypodermic needles, or during birth if the mother is Rh- and the baby is Rh+ (inherited from the father). The exchange at birth may occur due to a leakage of blood within the placenta, which normally tears during birth, into the mother's bloodstream. If the Rh-negative mother becomes pregnant again after the first delivery and exposure, and the second fetus is Rh+, her subsequently developed naturally acquired Rh antibodies may now enter that second fetus' bloodstream and attack fetal red blood cells. The tragic result is called **hemolytic disease of the newborn**, which can end the newborn's life soon after birth. To avoid this outcome, Rh- mothers are treated with an agent that prevents the mother from producing Rh antibodies.

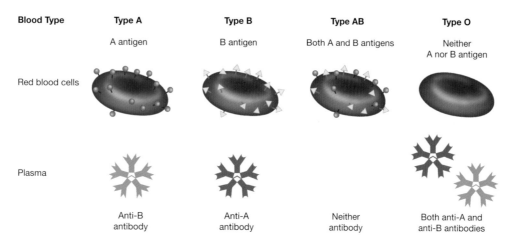

Blood Type	Type A	Type B	Type AB	Type O
Red blood cells	A antigen	B antigen	Both A and B antigens	Neither A nor B antigen
Plasma	Anti-B antibody	Anti-A antibody	Neither antibody	Both anti-A and anti-B antibodies

© bluedoor, LLC

Figure 10.1: The ABO system of blood typing.

Exercise 10.1: Blood Typing

Blood typing may be performed safely and quickly by using a test kit. Test kits contain antisera, which cause agglutination in non-compatible blood types. The antisera are usually mixtures that contain antibodies from mammals other than humans, and have been tested to work effectively with human blood. You will perform blood typing on glass slides or on test cards, whichever your instructor provides. The blood sample may be provided by your instructor, and may be an artificial blood substitute or animal blood. Alternatively, your instructor may authorize you to test your own blood. Whether using your own blood or that of an animal source, follow the safety precautions carefully: *Safety precaution: Wear disposable gloves and eye protection while performing blood tests. At the conclusion of the lab, place all contaminated materials (gloves, slides, toothpicks, etc.) into a biohazardous waste container, wipe down the countertops with 10% bleach solution, and thoroughly wash your hands with soap and water. If an accident occurs, notify your instructor immediately.*

1. Obtain two clean glass slides (or test cards), anti-A, anti-B, and anti-Rh typing sera, unused toothpicks, a marking pencil, and an Rh typing box. If you will be testing your own blood, also obtain a sterile lancet, alcohol swabs, and a medicine dropper.

2. Divide one slide into two halves with the marking pencil. On a small corner of the area, label half of the slide "anti-A", then place one drop of anti-A serum onto the center of the half slide. Label "anti-B" on the other half of the slide, using a small corner of the area only, then place one drop of anti-B serum onto its center. Place one drop of blood onto the drop of anti-A serum, and a drop of blood onto the anti-B serum.

3. Use a clean toothpick to mix the anti-A serum with the blood. Use a clean, unused toothpick to mix the anti-B serum with the blood (*do not use the same toothpick for both samples!*).

4. Allow 2 minutes for the reaction to occur, then observe your samples for agglutination (clumping or the presence of granulation), and record your results in the Data Table provided. Use **Figure 10.2** as a reference.

5. Label the second slide "anti-Rh" on a small corner only, then place one drop of anti-Rh serum onto its center. Place a drop of blood onto the anti-Rh serum, then mix with a clean, unused toothpick.

6. Place the slide in the Rh typing box to warm, and rock it gently to push the reaction.

7. Allow 2 minutes for the reaction to occur, then observe your sample for agglutination (clumping or the presence of granulation), and record your results in the Data Table provided.

8. **Clean-up:** All used toothpicks, glass slides and lancets/needles should be put into appropriate disposal containers. All other materials may be thrown in garbage or placed in green trays for washing. Clean lab benches with 10% bleach solution.

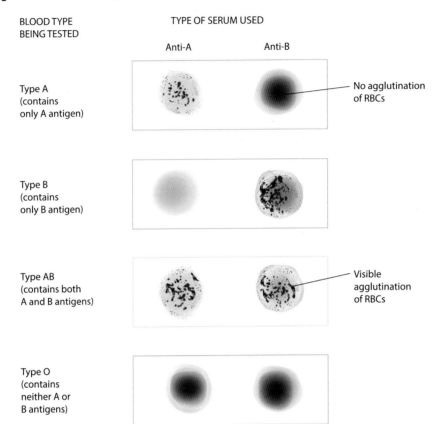

Figure 10.2: Blood typing in the ABO system.
The clumping is agglutination, which is a sign of incompatibility.

Data Table: Blood Typing

Agglutination Results	Yes	No
Clumping with anti-A		
Clumping with anti-B		
Clumping with anti-Rh		

ABO blood type of sample: _____

Rh blood type of sample: _____

What blood types can you safely donate blood to? _____

What blood types can you safely receive blood from? _____

Determining Hemoglobin

You have learned that **hemoglobin** is the large protein that occupies red blood cells. It is the vehicle that transports much of the oxygen within RBCs, and also participates in carbon dioxide transport. Therefore, a deficiency of hemoglobin synthesis results in an impairment of the blood's ability to transport oxygen, which is one cause of the general condition known as anemia. Technically, an individual can be anemic with a normal red blood cell concentration if the cells are deficient in hemoglobin. Because hemoglobin is the main factor in oxygen transport, the oxygen-carrying capacity of the blood can be evaluated by measuring hemoglobin content. A normal blood sample contains 12 to 18 grams of hemoglobin per 100 ml of blood; it is slightly higher in men (13 – 18g) than in women (12 – 16g). A reduced concentration of hemoglobin would result a reduced ability to transport oxygen to tissues (anemia) or hypothyroidism, cirrhosis of the liver, or blood loss. An elevated hemoglobin concentration can be seen in polycythemia or erythrocytosis, a condition that may be caused by congestive heart failure, obstructive pulmonary disease, and high altitudes.

Exercise 10.2: Determining Hemoglobin

Determining the hemoglobin content of blood by a clinical lab is usually performed with the use of a calibrated, accurate instrument called a hemoglobinometer. _Safety precaution: Wear disposable gloves and eye protection while performing blood tests. At the conclusion of the lab, place all contaminated materials (gloves, slides, toothpicks, etc.) into a biohazardous waste container, wipe down the countertops with 10% bleach solution, and thoroughly wash your hands with soap and water. If an accident occurs, notify your instructor immediately._

Hemoglobinometer Method

1. Obtain a sterile lancet, alcohol wipe, and a hemocue microcuvette. Keep the cuvette container closed when the container is not in use.

2. Wash and dry your hands and clean the end of your finger with an alcohol wipe. Use the lancet to prick your finger and wipe the first drop of blood away with the alcohol wipe. Squeeze your finger to obtain another drop of blood. Hold the cuvette on the square end and touch the pointed end the to the drop of blood. Allow the blood to fill the circle (optical eye) using capillary action.

3. Use a kimwipe to wipe to outside of the cuvette. If the circle (optical eye) is not filled completely, discard the microcuvette and obtain another sample.

4. Place the filled microcuvette in the cuvette holder of the hemoglobinometer. Close the cuvette holder. An hourglass will appear on the screen. After 15-60 seconds, the result will appear on the display.

5. Record your your results. _____ g/dl

   How do your results compare to normal results for a male or female? _____

   _____

   If your results are above or below normal, explain why this might be the case. _____

   _____

6. **Clean-up:** Hemolysis applicators should be put into appropriate disposal containers. it is your responsibility to remove the applicator from the hemoglobinometer. If blood gets on the lab bench, clean with a 10% bleach solution.

CHAPTER REVIEW

Name _____

Instructor _____

1. Centrifuging a blood sample separates the blood components into three layers in a centrifuge tube. The narrow middle layer:
   a. is called the buffy coat
   b. contains white blood cells
   c. contains platelets
   d. all of the above

2. The part of the blood that transports dissolved substances is the:
   a. red blood cells
   b. plasma
   c. interstitial fluid
   d. platelets

3. A cell in a blood smear that is larger than erythrocytes and contains pinkish-orange granules and a bilobed nucleus is called a:
   a. lymphocyte
   b. monocyte
   c. eosinophil
   d. neutrophil

4. When looking at a normal blood smear under the microscope, any field of view is dominated by the presence of:
   a. red blood cells
   b. lymphocytes
   c. white blood cells
   d. platelets

5. A blood smear contains irregularly shaped bodies that are stained dark. These bodies play a major role in:
   a. oxygen transport
   b. immunity
   c. blood clot formation
   d. all of the above

6. A differential white blood cell count from a patient's blood sample contains elevated numbers of lymphocytes that appear normal otherwise. This data suggests:
   a. leukemia
   b. viral infection
   c. anemia
   d. bacterial infection

7. Hematocrit results from a female patient is 20% as compared to a normal range of 37%–47%. This data indicates:
   a. polycythemia
   b. anemia
   c. the patient has a bacterial infection
   d. a brain tumor

8. A person with type O blood:
   a. has both A and B antigens
   b. lacks both A and B antigens
   c. lacks anti-A and anti-B antibodies
   d. cannot supply oxygen to cells

9. During a blood typing test, the sample blood clumps with antiserum type A (anti-A serum). What ABO blood type(s) is the sample? Select all that apply.
   a. type A
   b. type B
   b. type AB
   d. type O

10. During a coagulation time test, the blood of a patient begins to show fibrin threads about 10 minutes after its removal. This time duration suggests possible:

    a. impatience with the test   b. hemophilia

    b. anemia   d. polycythemia

APPLYING YOUR NEW KNOWLEDGE

1. The field of medicine that addresses diseases associated with blood is called hematology. A physician specializing in the treatment of blood disorders is known as a hematologist or, in some cases, a hematopathologist. Although you have experienced some of the "tools of the trade" that assist in a diagnosis, many other, more sophisticated tests are available. Based on the tests performed in the series of exercises in this chapter, describe the tests that you would employ if asked to develop a diagnosis of a patient complaining of a lack of energy, bleeding of the gums, and frequent bruising beneath the skin.

2. Synthetic blood substitutes are under development in many research labs across the country, and some are becoming available now. Discuss the potential advantages of the use of a synthetic blood substitute, and the potential disadvantages, if any.

3. You are working in the Emergency Room at Oakton Community Hospital. Two car accident victims are brought in at the same time. One of the victims, a 10 y/o female is severely bleeding from an external wound in the abdominal area; she is in need of receiving blood. The driver of the car, a 40 y/o male who is thought to be the child's father is suffering from an injury to the shoulder, but is not externally bleeding.

   You perform a quick blood-typing test on both patients with the following results:

   Patient 1: 10 y/o female

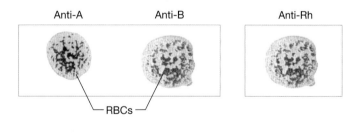

   Blood Type = _____

   Patient 2: 40 y/o male

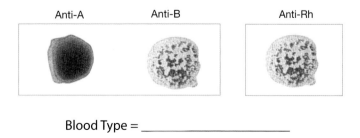

   Blood Type = _____

   Can the 10 y/o patient receive blood from the 40 y/o patient?
   Explain why or why not.

4. Polycythemia is a blood disorder characterized by an overproduction of red blood cells. Explain why this disorder is often seen in patients with congestive heart failure.

5. What symptoms might you expect to see in a female patient having a hemoglobin measurement of 10.5g/100ml blood?

   What are some possible causes of having the above hemoglobin measurement?

6. Discuss why the inhalation of automobile exhaust fumes can be potentially life threatening.

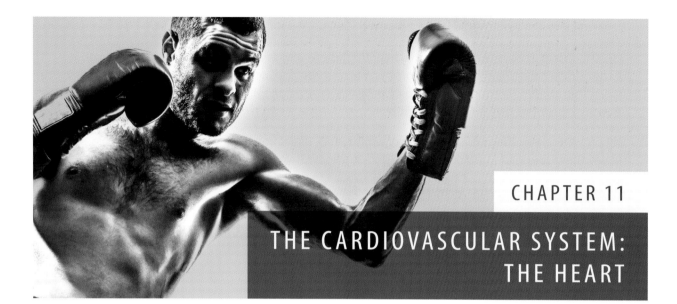

The **cardiovascular system** (*cardio* = heart, + *vascul* = little blood vessels) is composed of the blood, heart, and blood vessels. The system circulates blood throughout the body to bring it into close proximity to every living cell, providing a source of nourishment, waste removal, and delivering vital materials. The heart provides the propulsion of blood, and the blood vessels (arteries, capillaries, and veins) transport the blood in a closed loop circulation.

The heart is a fist-sized muscle within the chest that beats rhythmically throughout your lifetime. Through a series of lab exercises in this chapter, you will learn about its structure and the main features of its function.

The laboratory exercises in this unit correlate to Chapters 18 and 19 in your textbook and address the following BIO 232 course objectives:

1.   Correlate the conduction of an action potential through the heart with major components of an EKG

2.   Compare the mechanisms that regulate blood pressure

Exercise 11.1: Sheep or Pig Heart Dissection

You will dissect a preserved sheep or pig heart in this exercise as a comparison study to the anatomy of the human heart. _Safety precaution: always wear disposable gloves when dissecting to protect your hands from irritating chemicals in the preservative. Also, use the sharp instruments with care, and dispose all waste properly as directed by your instructor._

Obtain a preserved sheep or pig heart, a dissecting tray, dissection instruments, and disposable gloves. Rinse the heart in water to remove excess preservatives.

Examining the External Features of the Heart

To properly complete the heart dissection, you must become familiar with the external features of the heart. Knowing the external anatomy of the heart will help you understand where to begin and end the incisions you will be making.

Locating Features on the Ventral Side of the Heart

You will first locate major anatomical features on the ventral side of the heart. The ventral side is what you would see if you were to look at the heart from the bellyside of the pig. It is also important to note that from the ventral view the pig's right side will be on your left and the pig's left side will be on your right.

Note: As you follow the instructions, refer to the figure on the opposing page. The anatomical features are labeled on the figures. The numbers next to each feature correspond to the step that describes that feature.

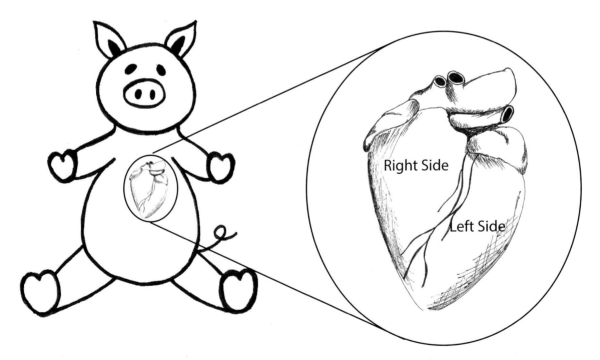

Figure 11.1: Ventral side of pig.

3. Locate the long groove that runs diagonally across the ventral side of the heart. This is the anterior longitudinal sulcus. Refer to **Figures 11.2** and **11.3**.
    - The anterior longitudinal sulcus separates the right and left ventricles.

4. Locate the ventricle to the right (your right) of the anterior longitudinal sulcus. This is the left ventricle (because it is on the pig's left).
    - The left ventricle receives oxygenated blood from the left atrium and pumps blood to the aorta.

5. Locate the ventricle to the left (your left) of the anterior longitudinal sulcus. This is the right ventricle.
    - The right ventricle receives deoxygenated blood from the right atrium and pumps blood to the pulmonary artery.

6. Locate the dark blood vessels that are embedded in the anterior longitudinal sulcus. These are the coronary blood vessels.
    - The coronary blood vessels supply the heart tissue with blood.

7. Locate the pointed bottom of the left ventricle. This is the apex. Refer to **Figures 11.2** and **11.3**.

8. Locate the two wrinkled pouch-like structures located at the top of the heart. These are the right auricle and the left auricle.
    - The auricles are outward extensions of the right atrium and left atrium.

    Tip: The auricles are the only part of the atria (plural for atrium) that you can see from the outside of the heart. After you cut the heart open, you will be able to distinguish the atria from the ventricles internally.

9. Locate the large topmost artery that has two other blood vessels branching from the top. This large blood vessel is the aorta.
    - The aorta carries oxygenated blood from the left ventricle to the entire body.

    Tip: Because the aorta twists around the pulmonary artery, it will look as though the aorta is coming from the right atrium when it is actually coming from the left ventricle.

10. Locate the first branch of the aorta after it leaves the heart. This is the brachiocephalic artery.
    - The brachiocephalic artery carries oxygenated blood to the head and right arm of the sheep or pig (equivalent to the human right upper limb).

    Tip: You may not be able to see the blood vessels because they have been cut off. Instead, you may just see holes where the branches of the arteries once were.

11. Locate the second branch of the aorta after it leaves the heart. This is the left subclavian artery.
    - The left subclavian artery carries oxygenated blood to the left forearm of the sheep or pig (equivalent to human left upper limb).

12. Locate the artery ascending from the right ventricle just below and in front of the aorta. This is the pulmonary artery.
    - The pulmonary artery carries deoxygenated blood from the right ventricle to the lungs.

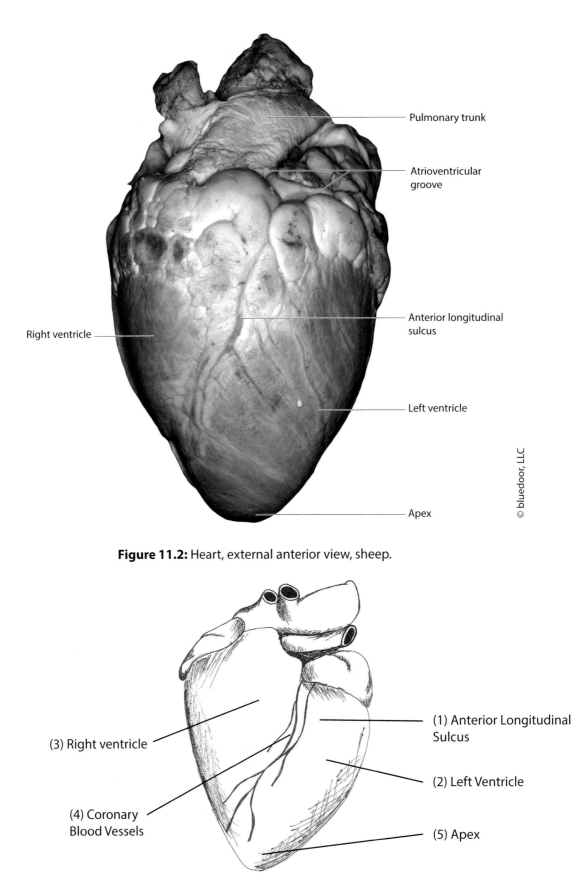

Pulmonary trunk

Atrioventricular
groove

Anterior longitudinal
sulcus

Right ventricle

Left ventricle

Apex

© bluedoor, LLC

Figure 11.2: Heart, external anterior view, sheep.

(1) Anterior Longitudinal
Sulcus

(3) Right ventricle

(2) Left Ventricle

(4) Coronary
Blood Vessels

(5) Apex

Figure 11.3: Ventral (anterior) view of Pig Heart (Features 1-5).

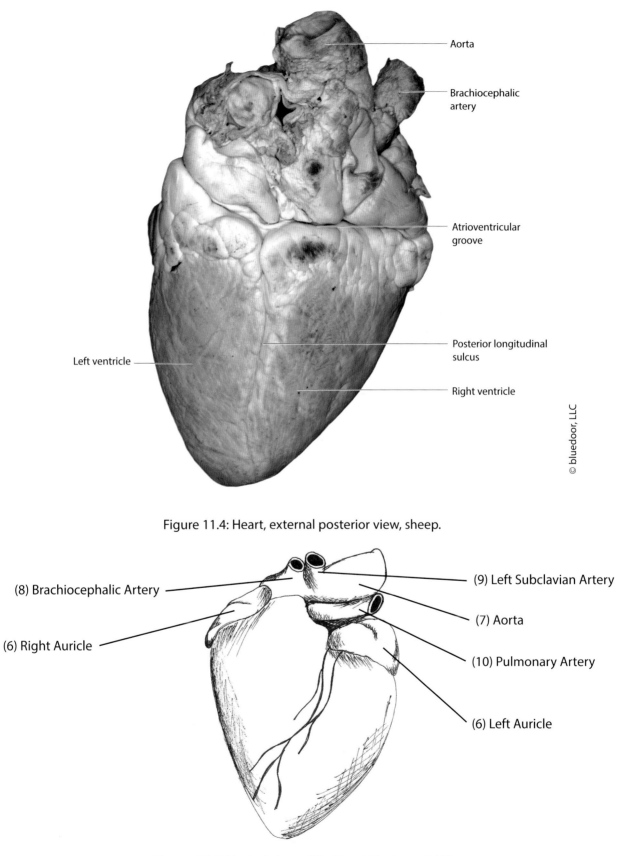

Figure 11.4: Heart, external posterior view, sheep.

Figure 11.5: Ventral view of Pig Heart (Features 6-10)

Locating Features on the Dorsal Side of the Heart

Flip the heart over to examine features on the dorsal (posterior) side of the heart. The dorsal side is what you would see if you were to look at the heart from the backside of the pig. It is also important to note that from the dorsal view your left and right are the same as the pig's left and right.

1. Locate the vein that can be seen above and to the left of the right auricle. This is the superior vena cava. Refer to **Figure 11.7**.

   • The superior vena cava brings deoxygenated blood from the upper body to the right atrium.

2. Insert a probe into the superior vena cava until the probe emerges from a lower opening.

   TIP: Do not insert the probe into the right atrium. Keep moving the probe around until you find the other opening on the surface of the heart.

3. Notice the opening from which the probe emerged. This vein, located below the superior vena cava and to the left of the right auricle, is the inferior vena cava.

   • The inferior vena cava brings deoxygenated blood from the lower body and merges with the superior vena cava before entering the right atrium.

   TIP: The venae cavae may have been cut off during preparation and only appear as holes.

4. Locate the pulmonary veins connected to the left atrium.

   • These four veins carry oxygenated blood from the lungs to the left atrium.

   TIP: The pulmonary veins may have been cut off also during preparation and appear as one or more large holes between the venae cavae and left atrium.

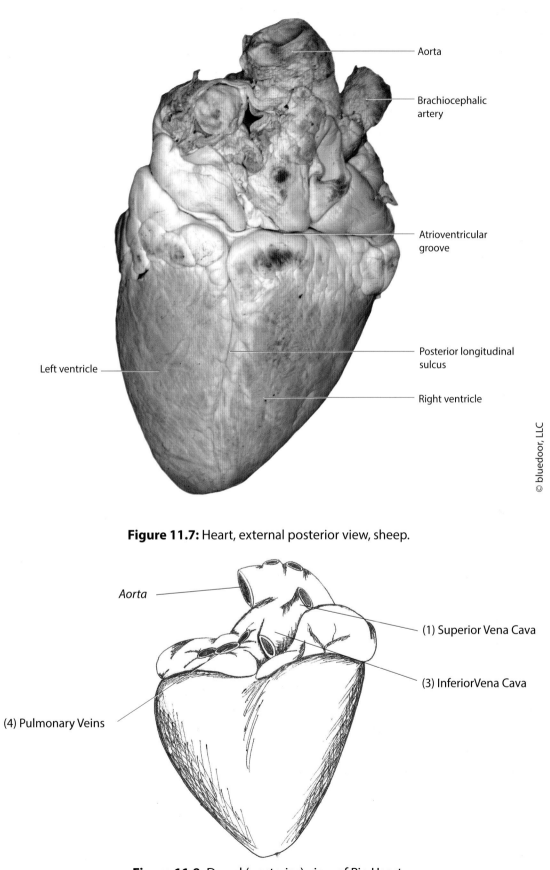

Figure 11.7: Heart, external posterior view, sheep.

Figure 11.8: Dorsal (posterior) view of Pig Heart.

Dissecting the Right Side of the Heart

This section will guide you through making three incisions in the right side of the heart. These incisions should allow you to examine the internal structures of the right atrium, right ventricle, pulmonary artery, superior vena cava, and inferior vena cava.

1. Flip the heart so the ventral side is toward you.

2. Make the first incision lengthwise through the pulmonary artery, beginning at the opening and ending slightly past where the pulmonary artery enters the right ventricle. (**Figure 11.10**.)

3. Spread open the pulmonary artery and look for the pulmonary semilunar valve.

    TIP: If you cannot see the semilunar valve, then make the cut slightly longer.

4. Count the number of cusps that you see in this valve.

    *   Cusps are the pouch-like flaps of the valve that prevent the backflow of blood.

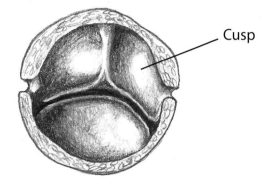

Cusp

Figure 11.9: Pulmonary Semilunar Valve.

5. Begin the second incision at the top of the right ventricle, ¾ to 1 inch left of the anterior longitudinal sulcus. Continue cutting parallel to the anterior longitudinal sulcus until you reach the dorsal side—about 2 inches above the apex. (**Figure 11.10**)

    TIP: Make sure that your scalpel is pointed straight down and that the wall of the right ventricle looks to be about ½ inch in thickness. Carefully cutting perpendicular to the surface of the heart muscle will prevent you from cutting into the heart at an angle.

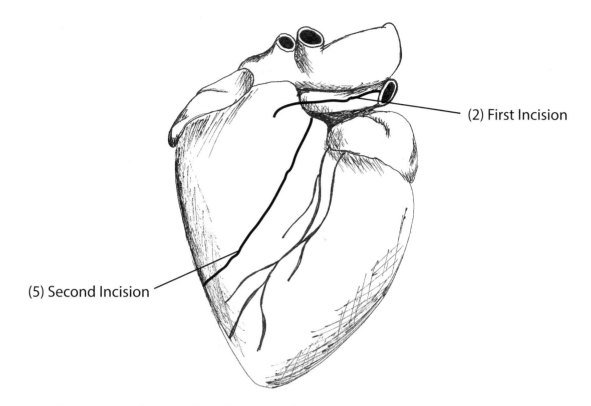

Figure 11.10: Anterior view of the heart: first and second incisions on the right side.

6. Flip the heart so the dorsal side is toward you. (**Figure 11.11**)

7. Begin your third incision at the top of the superior vena cava and make a straight cut through the right auricle and ventricle until you reach the end of the second incision.
    • The two incisions should connect.

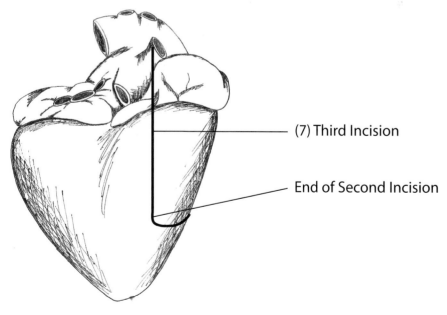

Figure 11.11: Third incision on the right side.

Examining the Internal Features of the Right Side

The incision you made in the previous section should allow you to spread open the right atrium and ventricle. The next step is to examine the internal structures of the right atrium, right ventricle, superior vena cava, and inferior vena cava.

1. Spread open the dorsal/posterior right side at levels of 2nd and 3rd incisions.

2. Examine the tricuspid valve between the right atrium and right ventricle.

3. Try to locate each cusp of the tricuspid valve. (**Figure 11.12**)

4. Locate the chordae tendineae.

    - Chordae tendineae are bands of fibrous tissue connecting the tricuspid valve cusps to the papillary muscle arising within the right ventricle.

5. Locate the papillary muscles, to which the chordae tendineae are attached.

    - Papillary muscles anchor the chordae tendineae.

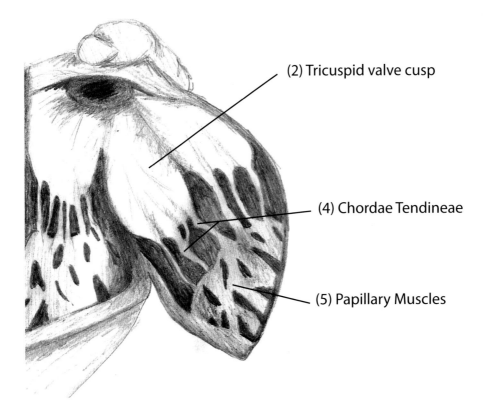

Figure 11.12: Internal view of the right side.

Dissecting and Examining the Left Side of the Heart

This section will guide you through making an incision in the left side of the heart, allowing you to examine the internal structures of the left atrium, left ventricle, and pulmonary veins. You will make a small incision in the aorta to view its internal features.

1. Turn the dorsal side of the heart toward you. (**Figure 11.14**)

2. Make a straight longitudinal incision beginning by the pulmonary veins immediately to the right of the left auricle, continuing through the left ventricle toward the apex.

3. Spread open the left side of the heart.

4. Compare the thickness of the left ventricle wall to the right ventricle wall.

5. Examine the bicuspid valve between the left atrium and ventricle.

6. Try to locate each cusp of the bicuspid valve.

7. Locate the chordae tendineae in the left ventricle.

8. Locate the papillary muscles in the left ventricle.

9. Make a lengthwise incision through the aorta beginning at the opening or cut end, and advance this cut down to the aortic valve.

10. Spread open the aorta and look down into the artery for the aortic semilunar valve.

    TIP: If you cannot see the aortic semilunar valve, then keep cutting lengthwise through the aorta until you can see the valve.

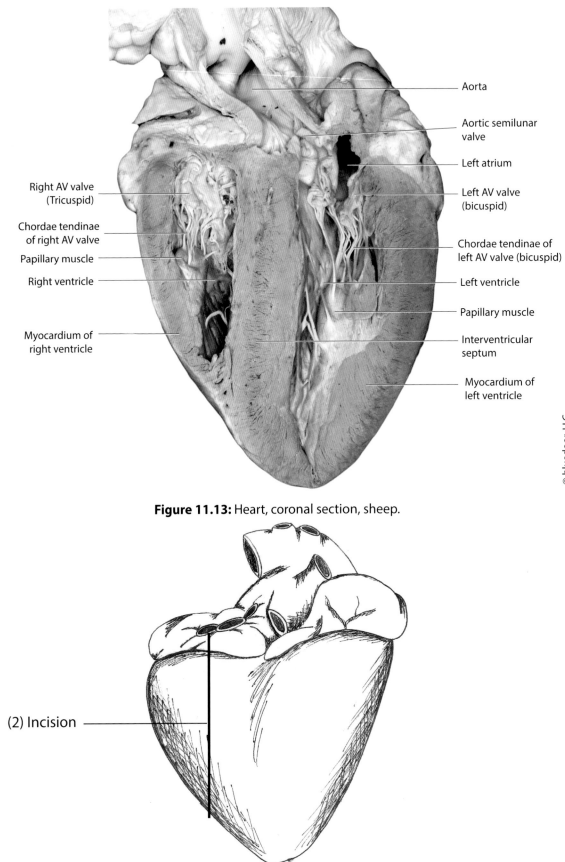

Figure 11.13: Heart, coronal section, sheep.

Aorta

Aortic semilunar valve

Left atrium

Left AV valve (bicuspid)

Chordae tendinae of left AV valve (bicuspid)

Left ventricle

Papillary muscle

Interventricular septum

Myocardium of left ventricle

Right AV valve (Tricuspid)

Chordae tendinae of right AV valve

Papillary muscle

Right ventricle

Myocardium of right ventricle

(2) Incision

Figure 11.14: Posterior view, incision on the left side.

11. Count the number of cusps that make up the aortic semilunar valve.

12. Feel the thick wall and smooth internal lining of the aorta.

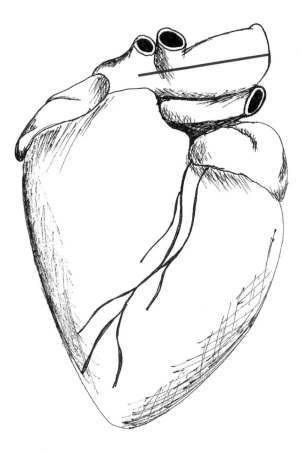

Figure 11.15: Incision of aorta.

13. **Clean-up:** Store dissected hearts in plastic bags. Make sure to put your name on the bag and put into green tray with instructor's name. Dispose of any unwanted tissue in the garbage can. Wash and dry dissection tools. Rinse and dry dissection trays. Reline trays with new paper towel.

PHYSIOLOGY OF THE HEART

The function of the heart is centered on its rhythmic contractions, which efficiently propel blood through the circulatory networks of the body. The contraction or systolic phases of the cardiac cycle commence with contraction of the atria, then relaxation of the atria, quickly followed by contraction of the ventricles (generating the peripheral pulse and arterial systolic pressure), then relaxation of the ventricles (resulting in the interval or arterial diastolic pressure). Most of a total cardiac cycle consists of diastole of the atria and ventricles, systole being only a short segment of the cycle. The contraction phase is called **systole** (*systole* = contraction), and the relaxation phase is known as **diastole** (*diastole* = spreading apart). In this part of the chapter, you will examine heart function by performing exercises that mainly involve clinical measurements of heart physiology.

Heart Sounds and Auscultation

The most common method of examining basic heart function is the popular procedure known as **auscultation** (*auscul* = listening). Auscultation is a physical examination that consists of listening to internal heart sounds using a stethoscope, which is an instrument that amplifies sound. During a heartbeat, the stethoscope can pick up two heart sounds, although four sounds are actually produced. The sounds are generated when the flow of blood strikes the heart valves, pushing them closed and causing turbulence. The first audible sound is referred to as **lubb**, or SI. It is produced by the sudden closure of the AV (mitral and tricuspid) valves during the initial phase of ventricular systole, simultaneous to the initial (exiting) out-flow of blood from the ventricles. The second sound is more brief and slightly sharper than the first, and is referred to as **dupp** (or dubb) or S2. This S2 occurs at the beginning of ventricular diastole, immediately after the end of ventricular systole, and is created by the sudden closure of the semilunar (aortic and pulmonary) valves. Basically, the S1 and S2 are sudden closures or the "slamming shut" of the AV and semilunar valves, respectively. During auscultation, you will hear lubb-dupp, pause, lubb-dupp, pause, lubb-dupp, pause, and so on. Each lubb-dupp sound represents one heartbeat, or cardiac cycle. Applying a stethoscope to the chest surface directly above a heart valve enables a focused listening to the function of that particular valve. **Heart rate** is the number of heartbeats in one minute. For most healthy individuals, the heart rate is between 70 and 80 beats per minute at rest, although the normal range is 60 to 100 beats per minute.

The most frequent condition that can be diagnosed by auscultation is called a **murmur**, which is a swishing sound that is usually caused by a backflow, or regurgitation, of blood. The most common cause of a murmur is a valvular defect. Another type of valvular defect that can be heard by auscultation is **stenosis**, which is the narrowing of a passage due to defects of one or more valves. Stenosis is usually heard as a high-pitched sound, or "screeching," as blood is pushed through narrow passages.

Exercise 11.2: Auscultation

In this exercise, you will work with a lab partner to learn auscultation as a measurement of heart activity.

1. Obtain a stethoscope and alcohol swabs. Clean the earpieces with an alcohol swab, and allow them to air dry.

2. Carefully place the earpieces into your ear canals. The earpieces should be pointed forward to make the fit comfortable. To check the fit, tap the bell (the round portion) gently and listen for the magnified tapping sound.

3. You are now ready to auscultate the heart. Ask your partner to find the superior border of their sternum by palpating the sternal (jugular) notch, then lower their touch about 2 inches and to the right one inch. Your partner should be palpating the 2nd intercostal space just to the right of the sternum. Ask your partner to place the bell of the stethoscope on this area to enable you to listen to the aortic valve of the heart.

4. Listening with the stethoscope, count the number of heartbeats in one minute, and record this figure as the heart rate at rest: _____.

5. Ask your lab partner if they have any known heart problems. If they do not, instruct your partner to run in place for 30 seconds. Auscultate the heart once more in the same location on the thorax, and count the number of heartbeats in one minute immediately following the exercise. Record this figure as the heart rate after exercise:

   _____

6. Which heart sound is louder at rest (lubb or dupp)? _____

   Which heart sound is louder after exercise? _____

   What effect does exercise have on heart rate, and for what purpose? _____

   _____

   _____

Pulse Rate

During a single heartbeat or cardiac cycle, the blood pushed into the arteries undergoes an alternation of pressure. Pressure drops during ventricular diastole, and rises during ventricular systole. The difference between diastolic and systolic pressure is called **pulse pressure**. Pulse pressure reaches a high point when the ventricles contract and generate a wave of pressure that travels through the arteries. Pulsations produced by the left ventricle can be felt by placing fingers on an artery near the skin. Pulsations counted in a one-minute interval of time yield the **pulse rate**. The most common superficial pulse points on the body include the common carotid artery, which can be felt at the side of the neck, the brachial artery in the antecubital fossa, the radial artery at the lateral aspect of the wrist (above the thumb), and the femoral artery in the groin; these pulse points and others are illustrated in **Figure 11.16**. The pulse rate averages 70 to 80 beats per minute at rest and normally, equals the heart rate, since the pulse rate is a determination of the contraction frequency of the left ventricle.

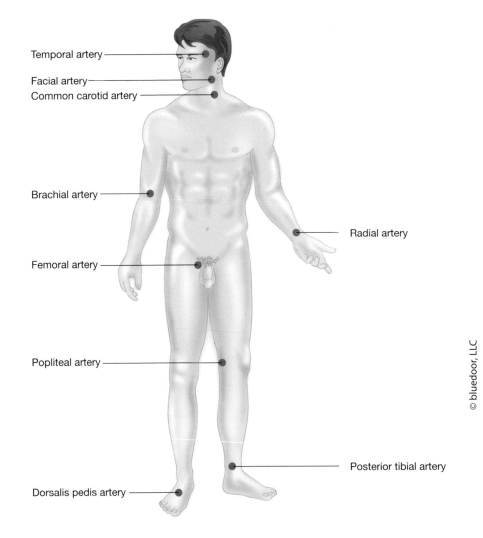

© bluedoor, LLC

Figure 11.16: Pulse points of the body.

Exercise 11.3: Measuring the Pulse

You will practice measuring the pulse rate by palpating the carotid artery and radial artery pulse points, both at rest and after mild exercise.

1. Locate the Adam's apple of your partner (the thyroid cartilage). Using your index and middle finger, press down on ONE side of the Adam's apple to palpate the carotid artery. Once you are able to feel the pulse, count the number of pulses in one minute and record the carotid pulse at rest: _____

2. Locate the shallow groove in your lab partner's wrist on the anterior side that is immediately medial to the radius (thumb side). Palpate the radial artery by pressing down onto this groove with your index and middle finger. Once you are able to feel the pulse, count the number of pulses in one minute and record the radial pulse at rest:

   _____

3. After checking to make sure your lab partner does not have a heart condition, instruct your partner to run in place for 30 seconds. Immediately check their carotid pulse for one minute and record the carotid pulse after exercise:

   _____

4. Repeat #3, but this time check the radial pulse after 30 seconds of exercise.

   Record the radial pulse after exercise: _____

5. Is there a measurable difference between carotid pulse rate and radial pulse rate?

   _____

   What is the effect of exercise upon the pulse rate? _____

   _____

   Compare the pulse rates with the heart rates measured in Exercise 11.2. Do you see a difference between the two figures at rest? _____

   Do you see a difference between heart rate and pulse rate after exercise?

Class experiment: Effect of Caffeine on Heart Rate

In this experiment, you will investigate the effect of caffeine on the human heart rate.

Divide the class into two groups:

> Group 1: Control – drinks 355 ml of a diet, caffeine free beverage
>
> Group 2: Experimental – drinks 355 ml of a diet, caffeinated beverage

1. For all participants, sit quietly in a chair for five minutes (do not stand or walk around)

2. After this relaxation period, take your resting heart rate while sitting down. Record the number of heartbeats per minute. For accuracy, do NOT record your heart rate over shorter periods of time and extrapolate to determine heart rate.

3. Step out of lab and drink 355 ml (=12 ounces) of your designated beverage. Do this as quickly as you can and finish the beverage in under 3 minutes.

4. Remain at rest in your chair for an additional 15 minutes. After the fifteen minutes, record your heart rate as you did in #2 above.

5. Record your readings in the class data table.

Student	Heart Rate			
	Non-Caffeine Before Ingestion	Non-Caffeine 15 Min. After Ingestion	Caffeine Before Ingestion	Caffeine 15 Min. After Ingestion
Averages				

ANALYSIS:

1. For both the control and the experimental groups, graph the difference in heart rate (not averages).

2. Using your bar graph, summarize in words the effect of caffeine on heart rate within your class.

3. Discuss the mechanism by which caffeine has an impact on heart rate.

Exercise 11.4: Electrocardiography

You will perform the procedure of electrocardiography on a subject in your lab as a review of the concepts of cardiovascular physiology. In the first step, you will prepare the subject. The second step will record the ECG on your subject at rest, after holding the breath, and during mild exercise. In the third step, you will perform calculations that evaluate the ECG data. The following describes the procedures using a standard electrocardiograph. If the equipment in your lab is different, follow the instructions provided in the operator's manual or provided by your instructor instead (particularly for step #2).

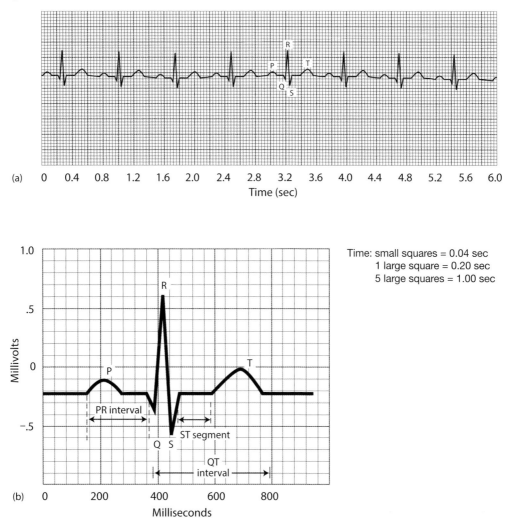

Figure 11.17: The normal electrocardiogram. (a) Normal sinus rhythm. (b) A recording of a single cardiac cycle.

1. Preparing the subject

   a. Identify a subject, and scrub the skin at the following attachment sites with an alcohol swab: 1) at the anterior surface of each forearm 2–3 inches above the wrist, and 2) at the anterior surface of each leg about 2–3 inches above the lateral malleolus.

   b. Apply electrode paste to the swabbed skin surfaces and place an electrode on each area.

   c. Attach the labeled tips of the patient cable to the corresponding electrodes. The leads should be marked RA for right arm, LA for left arm, LL for left leg, and RL for right leg. As shown in **Figure 11.18**, the RL (right leg) lead will serve as the ground and is not experimental, so you will record ECGs using three experimental leads.

   d. Position your subject comfortably in a supine (lying back) position, either on a cot or sitting relaxed on a chair.

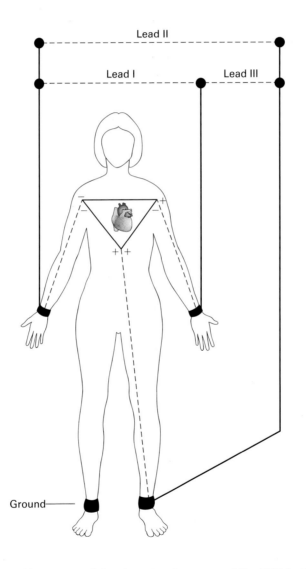

© bluedoor, LLC

Figure 11.18: Placement of the three leads to record the ECG in the lab.

2. Recording the ECGs

   a. Now that your subject is ready, you will perform a baseline (at rest) ECG recording. Turn on the power switch of the electrocardiograph and adjust the sensitivity to the lowest level (usually 1). Set the paper speed to 25 mm/sec and the lead selector to the position corresponding to recording from the #1 lead (RA-LA).

   b. Adjust the control knob to the RUN position (or its equivalent), and record the subject's ECG at rest from lead 1 for 2 minutes or until the recording becomes repeatable. As you do so, make sure your subject remains still and relaxed. Otherwise, electrical activity from skeletal muscles may be picked up and recorded as a false recording.

   c. Stop the recording. On the paper, label the recording "lead 1."

   d. Repeat the procedures #1 and #2 above for lead 2 (RA-LL) and once more for lead 3 (LA-LL).

   e. With the baseline ECG established, you may now try the ECG during breath holding. Begin by positioning the same subject in the sitting position. Use lead 1, set the paper speed to a rate of 25 mm/sec, and start the recording by turning the control knob to the RUN position. Instruct your subject to begin holding the breath. After one minute, stop the recording and remind your subject to resume breathing. On the paper, label the recording "breath holding lead 1."

   f. Now you may record an ECG on your subject during exercise. Check the electrodes on your subject to make sure they are securely attached to the skin. Use lead 1 once again, check that the paper speed is set to a rate of 25 mm/sec, and start the recording by turning the control knob to the RUN position. Immediately instruct your subject to stand up and run in place for 3 minutes. At the end of this time period instruct your subject to sit down, but continue to record for an additional 3 minutes. Stop the recording after 3 minutes of rest, and label the recording "exercise lead 1."

3. Calculations of the ECG recordings

   a. Because the printed paper speed for all recordings was set at 25 mm/sec, a distance of 1 mm (one small square on ECG paper) is equivalent to 0.04 seconds. To calculate **heart rate**, measure the distance between the start of one P wave to the start of the next P wave. You can do this easily by counting the number of small squares. Then multiply the number of squares counted by 0.04 seconds. The product will give you the time in seconds for one heartbeat, which is the length of one cardiac cycle, in seconds/beat. Because there are 60 seconds in one minute, divide 60 by the length of one cardiac cycle. For example: If you counted 20 squares (or 20 mm) from P wave to P wave, .04 seconds X 20 mm = 0.8 sec/beat; 60 sec/min/0.8 sec/beat = 75 beats/min

   b. Calculate heart rate in this manner for each of your recordings, and complete the Data Table provided below with your calculations.

   c. In addition to heart rate measurements, an ECG provides information that can lead to the diagnosis of a heart condition. For example, the P-Q interval (also referred to as PR interval) is the time between atrial and ventricular depolarization, normally between 0.12 and 0.2 seconds. A P-Q interval longer than 0.2 seconds is evidence of a heart block due to AV node or AV bundle damage that results in a delay of action potentials reaching the ventricular myocardium. A normal QRS complex ranges from 0.06 to 0.10 seconds. If the complex lasts longer than 0.12 seconds, a right or left bundle branch block may have occurred, causing the ventricles to contract asynchronously. From the data you have collected, measure the length of the P-Q interval in each recording, multiply this distance by 0.04 seconds to determine the length in seconds, and record your calculations in the Data Table. Repeat the measurements for the QRS complex and convert to seconds, then record your findings in the Data Table.

Data Table: ECG

ECG Recording	Heart Rate (beats/min)	P-Q Interval (sec)	QRS complex (sec)
Lead 1			
Lead 2			
Lead 3			
Breath Holding Lead 1			
Exercise Lead 1			

4. What conclusions can you make about the difference in heart rate among at rest, holding the breath, and mild exercise in your subject?

_____

_____

5. Explain why measuring the P-Q interval and QRS complex can provide information on possible conditions of the heart conduction system.

_____

_____

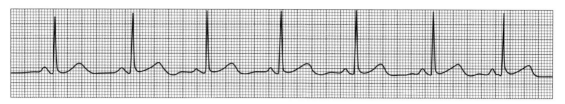

(a) Normal sinus rhythm

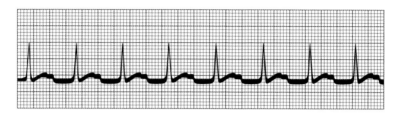

(b) Note: slow ventricular contraction

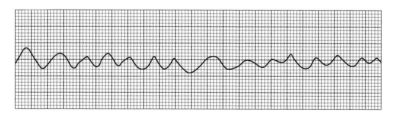

(c) Note: slow heart rhythm

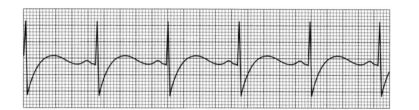

(d) Note: Complete disruption of cardiac cycle

Figure 11.19: Electrocardiographs.

CHAPTER REVIEW

Name _____

Instructor _____

1. The pericardium:

    a. is a serous membrane enclosing the heart
    b. is a thick membrane with four layers
    c. includes the myocardium
    d. forms the inner heart wall

2. The portion of the heart wall that dominates its volume and provides the propulsion of blood is called the:

    a. left ventricle
    b. epicardium
    c. myocardium
    d. endocardium

3. As blood flows through the heart, it must pass through the _____ before entering the right ventricle.

    a. left ventricle
    b. pulmonary valve
    c. tricuspid valve
    d. bicuspid valve

4. In the sheep heart, the heart chamber with the thickest wall is the:

    a. right atrium
    b. left atrium
    c. right ventricle
    d. left ventricle

5. The dominant tissue of the heart can be distinguished from other tissues under the microscope by the presence of:

    a. intercalated discs between cells
    b. striations
    c. many nuclei
    d. a large amount of cytoplasm

6. The string-like structures that anchor AV valves to papillary muscles are called:

    a. trabeculae carneae
    b. chordae tendineae
    c. pectinate muscles
    d. seimlunar valves

7. The portion of the heart conduction system that initiates each cardiac cycle is the:

    a. sinoatrial node
    b. AV bundle branch
    c. AV node
    d. purkinje fibers

8. In an ECG, ventricular depolarization, which precedes ventricular systole, is recorded as the:

    a. only wave deflection
    b. P wave
    c. QRS complex
    d. T wave

9. A common goal among fitness experts and athletes is:

    a. fibrillation
    b. tachycardia
    c. bradycardia
    d. normal sinus rhythm

10. Each of the following are arteries where the pulse can be felt **except** the:

    a. radial artery
    b. axillary artery
    c. femoral artery
    d. common carotid artery

APPLYING YOUR NEW KNOWLEDGE

1. The most common disease affecting the function of the heart is atherosclerosis, in which coronary arteries become clogged with smooth muscle, fat, blood clots, and cholesterol deposits resulting in a reduction of blood flow to the myocardium. When the restriction in blood flow begins to affect cardiac cell function, the pain generated is called angina pectoris. With decreasing blood flow, lack of oxygen results in death of cardiac cells and this tissue death is referred to as myocardial infarction, commonly termed "heart attack." This infarction or death of cardiac tissue can result in reduction in cardiac muscle function and disturbances in conduction (e.g. irregular heart rhythm or arrhythmias). When the result of MI is total cessation of cardiac activity, i.e., cardiac arrest, the patient will not recover and death will occur unless successful resuscitation (CPR) is instituted promptly. Current treatment for atherosclerosis includes the insertion of stents, which force the clogged vessels to open wider, and coronary artery bypass grafts. Describe in your own words how the insertion of a stent would prevent a heart attack. How can coronary bypass grafts prevent heart attacks?

2. You have learned in this chapter that the ECG is performed to detect problems in heart function. In Figure 11.18, abnormal ECGs are shown next to a normal ECG. Make a rough diagnosis of the ECGs in Figures 11.20b, 11.20c, 11.20d.

3. Aortic stenosis is a condition in which the aortic semilunar valve is constricted or narrowed. This condition causes diminished left ventricular stroke volume. Upon evaluation of an echocardiogram, it is noted that the left ventricle is abnormally large in size (= hypertrophy).

   Explain how aortic stenosis could cause left ventricular hypertrophy.

   Explain how aortic stenois could cause a decrease in arterial systolic blood pressure.

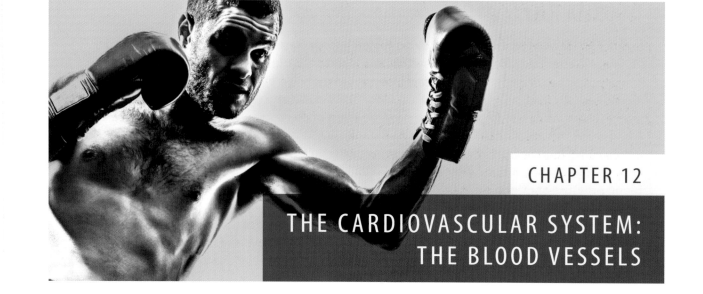

CHAPTER 12

THE CARDIOVASCULAR SYSTEM: THE BLOOD VESSELS

You have learned that the cardiovascular system is composed of the blood, heart, and blood vessels, and that its function is the distribution of blood to all body cells, supplying the cells with oxygen, nutrients, hormones, and enzymes, and removing carbon dioxide and other waste materials. The blood vessels (arteries, capillaries, and veins) provide the thoroughfare for the flow of blood, and larger elastic arteries assist in its propulsion. Arteries carry blood away from the heart, branching into smaller and smaller tributaries, eventually resulting in microscopic capillaries. The exchange of materials between the bloodstream and the interstitial fluid occurs only across the thin walls of the minute capillaries. Capillaries converge to form tiny veins, which become larger as they collect blood from larger areas of the body. The veins return blood to the heart for its recirculation.

The laboratory exercises in this unit correlate to Chapter 19 in your textbook and address the following BIO 232 course objectives:

1. Compare the mechanisms that regulate blood pressure
2. Compare vessels of circulation by anatomy and physiology

BLOOD PRESSURE

In order for blood to flow through the blood vessels, a force must be present to give it propulsion. This force is established by ventricular systole, and is known as **blood pressure**. The pressure is exerted by the collision of blood against blood vessel walls. It is at its highest level within the ascending aorta, and decreases gradually as blood flows away from the heart and into smaller arteries. Once inside arterioles, the blood pressure drops significantly, and continues to decline as blood enters capillaries, then venules, and finally veins. In the large veins merging with the right atrium and within the right atrium during atrial diastole, the pressure reaches a value of zero. The enormous difference in blood pressure between the aorta and the right atrium is known as the **blood pressure gradient**, and it is what causes blood to flow throughout the systemic circulation. Similarly, the blood pressure gradient between the pulmonary trunk and the left atrium causes blood to flow to the lungs and back to the heart. The rhythmic contractions of the heart result in a pulsation of blood pressure in the large elastic arteries. During ventricular systole, the pressure reaches its highest point, known as the **systolic blood pressure**. During ventricular diastole, blood pressure reaches it lowest point, which is called the **diastolic blood pressure**.

The clinical measurement of blood pressure is a common procedure routinely performed as a diagnostic tool. The arterial blood pressure can be measured directly or indirectly. The direct method, less common, involves insertion of a tube/pressure transducer directly into the artery. The more common indirect method employs the familiar **sphygmomanometer** consisting of an inflatable cuff (applied to the arm) attached to a pressure gauge (**Figure 12.1**). The gauge is a manometer, which measures a column of mercury as it rises in a tube in response to pressure from the inflated cuff, providing a physical measurement of the amount of pressure exerted to move the mercury. The measurement is recorded in millimeters of mercury (mm Hg). The band is inflated to a pressure higher than systolic pressure in order to cut off circulation to the forearm. Pressure is gradually released from the band, permitting blood to flow back into the forearm. The return of blood flow produces tapping sounds, called **Korotkoff sounds**, which can be heard with a stethoscope. The pressure on the gauge at the point the first soft tapping sounds are detected is the systolic pressure. As pressure is released further from the band, blood flow increases in turbulence to produce louder Korotkoff sounds. Pressure is gradually reduced, until eventually enough pressure is released from the band to allow the free flow of blood, at which point the sounds can no longer be heard; this pressure is recorded as the diastolic pressure.

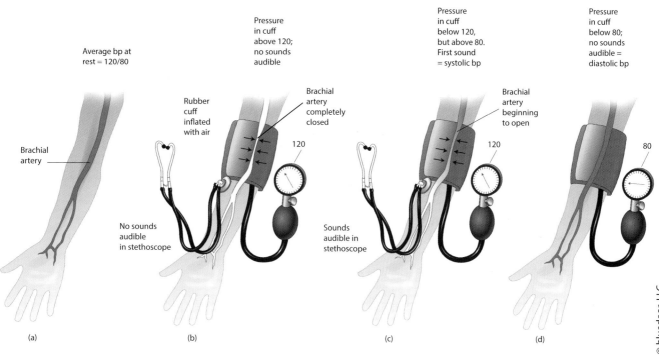

Average bp at
rest = 120/80

Brachial
artery

(a)

Rubber
cuff
inflated
with air

Pressure
in cuff
above 120;
no sounds
audible

Brachial
artery
completely
closed

120

No sounds
audible
in stethoscope

(b)

Pressure
in cuff
below 120,
but above 80.
First sound
= systolic bp

Brachial
artery
beginning
to open

120

Sounds
audible in
stethoscope

(c)

Pressure
in cuff
below 80;
no sounds
audible =
diastolic bp

80

(d)

© bluedoor, LLC

Figure 12.1: Measuring blood pressure with the sphygmomanometer. (a) Location of the brachial artery. (b) Placement of the band and inflation, which cuts off blood flow through the brachial artery. (c.) Slow deflation of the cuff allows blood to move through the artery, producing Korotkoff sounds. (d) Once the cuff pressure drops below 70 mm Hg, Korotkoff sounds stop.

Exercise 12.1: Measuring Blood Pressure at Rest

You will practice the measurement of arterial blood pressure by using a sphygmomanometer with the help of a lab partner in this exercise. You will also perform calculations that will evaluate pulse pressure and mean arterial pressure.

1. Working with a lab partner, obtain a stethoscope, a sphygmomanometer, and alcohol swabs. Swab the earpieces of the stethoscope to sanitize them, then examine the cuff of the sphygmomanometer to make sure air is not trapped in the cuff that might cause false measurements.

2. Instruct your lab partner to sit comfortably, with one arm resting on the lab bench as close to the level of the heart as possible. Wrap the sphygmomanometer cuff around either upper arm of your partner, with the inflatable part on the medial arm surface (**Figure 12.1**). If the cuff you are using is marked with an arrow, position the arrow over the brachial artery. Pull the cuff until it fits snugly around the arm, and secure it by bringing the Velcro ends together.

3. With your forefinger and middle finger, palpate the brachial pulse in the antecubital fossa, and mark the pulse point with a marking pencil. The brachial artery is in the anterior side of the arm just superior to the antecubital fossa and medial to the biceps brachii. Palpate the most superficial location of this brachial pulse and place the stethoscope bell over this point.

4. Inflate the cuff to a pressure level between 160 and 180 mm Hg, then open the valve and allow the cuff to deflate very slowly. With the stethoscope, listen carefully for the first tapping sound while keeping your eyes on the pressure gauge. Record the pressure at the onset of the tapping sound as the systolic pressure in the Data Table provided. Continue to deflate the cuff slowly.

5. Soon after the tapping sound begins, the sound will increase, then reduce to a slight tapping, then stop. Record the pressure when the last faint sound is heard as the diastolic pressure into the Data Table.

6. Repeat steps #1 through #5 two times to obtain three measurements. After ending each measurement, make sure you deflate the cuff completely before beginning the next measurement. Calculate the average measurement and record it in the Data Table.

7. Change places with your lab partner and repeat steps #1 through #6 to obtain blood pressure readings of a second subject, and record the values in the Data Table.

Data Table: Blood pressure at rest

Test	Systolic Pressure	Diastolic Pressure
Subject 1:		
Test #1	_____	_____
Test #2	_____	_____
Test #3	_____	_____
Average	_____	_____
Subject 2:		
Test #1	_____	_____
Test #2	_____	_____
Test #3	_____	_____
Average	_____	_____

Exercise 12.2: Measuring Blood Pressure Adjustments

The blood pressure is not a constant value but changes with the demands of the body to assure the continual movement of blood to tissues and organs. Factors that increase blood pressure include a rapid change in body position, exercise, and emotional stress. Adjusting blood pressure to meet changing demands by the body is achieved by altering the cardiac output (CO), which is the amount of blood pumped out of the left ventricle per unit of time, and/or peripheral resistance (PR), which is the ability of blood to flow through blood vessels (mainly arterioles). Peripheral resistance is altered by the vasoconstriction and vasodilation of arterioles. In this exercise, you will investigate how different factors can alter or influence the blood pressure.

Change in Body Position:

1. Measure the blood pressure and pulse rate of your partner while he/she reclines, then repeat the measurements when he/she stands up. Record results.

	Arterial Pressure Systolic/ Diastolic	Pulse Rate Per Minute
Lying Down		
Standing		

Questions:

1. When your partner stood up, what happened to the relative blood volumes in his/her neck, chest and legs?

2. What happened to the heart rate and blood pressure when your partner went from the supine to the upright position? What do you think happened to peripheral vascular resistance (blood vessel diameters)?

3. How quickly did this happen?

4. How do you explain this change?

Exercise:

1. You will perform a blood pressure measurement on two subjects, one who is in good physical fitness and another who admittedly is not. Identify subject #1 as a volunteer who is in good physical fitness and confirms that exercise will not pose health risks to them. Repeat instructions #1 through #5 in Exercise 12.1 to obtain a blood pressure measurement at rest. Then instruct your subject to perform an exercise for roughly 5 minutes, such as running in place, stepping up and down on a bench, or walking briskly up and down a stairway. After 5 minutes of exercise, instruct your subject to sit down and immediately measure and record the systolic and diastolic blood pressure values in the Data Table provided. Repeat this procedure three times and calculate and record the average pressures. Then identify subject #2 as a volunteer who is not in good physical condition and confirms that exercise will not pose health risks to them. Obtain blood pressure measurements at rest and immediately after 5 minutes of exercise, as you did with subject #1. Record your results in the Data Table provided. Repeat this procedure three times and calculate and record the average pressures.

Data Table: Adjustments in blood pressure

Test Subject 1:	Resting Systolic/Diastolic BP	After excercise Systolic/Diastolic BP
Test #1	_____	_____
Test #2	_____	_____
Test #3	_____	_____
Average	_____	_____

| Test | Resting | After excercise |
Subject 2:	Systolic/Diastolic BP	Systolic/Diastolic BP
Test #1	_____	_____
Test #2	_____	_____
Test #3	_____	_____
Average	_____	_____

2. How does the first subject's blood pressure compare with that of subject #2 at rest?

    _____

    How do they compare after exercise? _____

    _____

    What can you conclude are the benefits of physical fitness?

    _____

    _____

Temperature:

This test is used to demonstrate the effect of a stimulus such as cold temperature on blood pressure. Volunteer should not have any cold sensitivities (e.g. Reynaud's Phenomenon) and confirms that immersing their hand in cold water will not pose any health risks to them.

1. Have your partner sit down comfortably.
2. Record the systolic and diastolic blood pressure while in a resting state.
3. Immerse your partner's free hand in ice water (approx. 5 degrees C) to a depth well above the wrist.
4. After 15-20 seconds in the cold, measure your partner's blood pressure every 30 seconds for about 2 minutes.
5. Record results.

	Arterial Pressure Systolic/Diastolic
Rest	
15-20 Seconds After Cold Immersion	
30 Seconds Later	
30 Seconds Later	
30 Seconds Later	
30 Seconds Later	

QUESTIONS

1. What is the immediate effect of cold immersion on arterial blood pressure?

2. Does the blood pressure return to normal following withdrawl of the hand from the ice water and, if so, how long did it take for the BP to return to normal?

3. Explain the physiological mechanisms behind your results.

CHAPTER REVIEW

Name _____

Instructor _____

1. From arterioles, blood flows into:

   a. venules

   b. larger arterioles

   c. capillaries

   d. the interstitial fluid

2. The superficial blood vessels on the dorsal surface of your hand contain valves and bleed slowly when cut. Therefore, you can identify them as:

   a. veins

   b. capillaries

   c. muscular arteries

   d. none of the above

3. The systemic arterial circulation:

   a. consists of tributaries from the aorta

   b. includes the brachial and radial arteries

   c. carries oxygenated blood

   d. all of the above

4. The brachiocephalic vein drains blood from the shoulder region via the:

   a. brachial vein

   b. femoral artery

   c. azygous vein

   d. subclavian vein

5. The pulmonary arteries:

   a. are part of the systemic arterial circulation

   b. carry blood to the pulmonary trunk

   c. carry oxygenated blood

   d. none of the above

6. Exercise normally causes arterial blood pressure to immediately:

   a. increase

   b. stop completely

   c. decrease

   d. fluctuate

7. What effect do the following have on blood pressure? (Use "I" for increase and "D" for decrease.)

   _____ increased diameter of arterioles

   _____ hemorrhage

   _____ increased cardiac output

   _____ increased pulse rate

   _____ exercise

   _____ systemic vasoconstriction

APPLYING YOUR NEW KNOWLEDGE

1. Explain why a physical fitness plan that causes a reduction of blood pressure is beneficial to cardiovascular health. In your answer, describe the association between blood pressure, pulse rate, and the cardiac cycle.

2. You learned in this section that exercise causes a temporary increase in blood pressure. Explain why the increase is a normal phenomenon and why it occurs.

3. You are working in the cardiac unit at Oakton Community Hospital. One of the patients is a 72 y/o female who has recently undergone emergency triple bypass surgery. She survived the surgery, however is now aware of some chronic cardiac condtions that she wasn't aware of before the emergency such as chronic hypertension and moderate atherosclerosis. Her cardiologist prescribed both beta blockers and alpha blockers. She and her family would like to understand the mechanisms by which these types of medications could help her condition. Beta blockers are drugs that block epinephrine and norepinephrine from binding to their beta-1 receptors in cardiac muscle tissue and reduce renal output of rennin. Alpha blockers block epinephrine and norepinephrine from binding to their beta-2 receptors in blood vessel walls. Explain three mechanisms by which this combination of medications can help manage this patient's chronic hypertension.

   (*Hint* Think about the cardiovascular effects of epinephrine and norepinephrine).

4. Interpret 150/85

CHAPTER 13

THE RESPIRATORY SYSTEM

The **respiratory system** brings oxygen into the bloodstream, from which it can be transported to all body cells. The system gets its name from its function: the process of providing cells with oxygen is commonly known as **respiration**. In addition to bringing oxygen to the bloodstream, the respiratory system also removes the waste product carbon dioxide from the blood and channels it outside the body. The respiratory system's primary organs are the two lungs, but the system includes additional organs: the nose, pharynx, larynx, and tracheobronchial tree, which conduct air into and out of the lungs.

The laboratory exercises in this unit correlate to Chapter 22 in your textbook and address the following BIO 232 course objectives:

1. Analyze the events involved in inspiration and expiration
2. Analyze the role of the urinary and respiratory systems in regulating blood and urine pH

PHYSIOLOGY OF THE RESPIRATORY SYSTEM

The function of the respiratory system consists of a three-step process. The first step, inhalation or **inspiration**, is completed when respiratory muscles contract resulting in air moving from the outside environment to the tiny alveoli within the lungs. Exhalation or **expiration** occurs when these same muscles relax, forcing air outwards. Inspiration and expiration, together, are referred to as **pulmonary ventilation**. The second step of respiratory function occurs when air has filled the lungs and has distributed to the level of the alveoli. Here, air molecules now diffuse between the alveoli and adjacent capillaries of the pulmonary circulation: oxygen passes from the alveoli to the capillaries and carbon dioxide passes from the capillaries to the alveoli. This exchange of oxygen and carbon dioxide at the level of this alveolus-capillary junction is known as **external respiration**. The third step of respiratory function, **internal respiration**, occurs when the oxygen, delivered to the tissue, diffuses into the body's cells and, simultaneously, carbon dioxide is transferred from the cells into the capillary bloodstream.

Respiratory Sounds

The flow of air into and out of the lungs as you breathe produces characteristic sounds that can be heard with the use of a stethoscope through auscultation, and which are often used to help in the diagnosis of a condition affecting ventilation. Two types of sounds can be heard: **bronchial sounds**, which are sounds like the rushing of air through a narrow space produced by air movement through the trachea and bronchi, and **vesicular breathing sounds**, which sounds like a rustling of leaves during a breezy day. Vesicular breathing sounds are produced by air rushing through bronchioles and filling the alveoli. Both sounds are less pronounced during a respiratory illness that reduces air flow, and they sometimes reach high pitch to produce wheezing or whistling sounds. A trained health specialist may also tap the chest wall, known as percussion, to note the tone of the echo of the underlying anatomy. A relatively clear, resonant, or hollow-sounding echo is a healthy sign, but a dull "solid" muffled echo may suggest inflammation (as in pneumonia), fluid, or the presence of solid objects, such as tumors.

Exercise 13.1: Respiratory Sounds

Using a stethoscope and the listening procedure of auscultation, you will listen to the respiratory sounds of your lab partner in this exercise.

1. Obtain a stethoscope and sanitize the earpieces with an alcohol swab. Allow the alcohol to dry before placing the earpieces into your ear canals.

2. With the stethoscope in place, place the bell of the stethoscope on the anterior neck of your subject just below the thyroid cartilage of the larynx. Listen for bronchial sounds during a normal breathing rhythm. Describe the sound: _____

    _____

3. Place the bell of the stethoscope against the outer wall of the chest at various locations, including various intercostal spaces and under the clavicle. Listen for the vesicular breathing sounds during normal inspiration, and describe them:

    _____

Respiratory Volumes

Respiratory volumes refer to the amount of air within the lungs during normal breathing movements or forced breathing movements. The average volumes for a man and a woman of average height and weight are listed in **Table 13.1**. Keep in mind that these volumes are averages. The volumes do vary according to each individual's height, weight, gender, physical fitness, age, race, and overall health. When performing a physical examination, these normal values are compared with measured volumes of the patient in an effort to determine the relative health of the respiratory function. The measurable values include:

- **Tidal volume (TV)**: The volume of air inhaled or exhaled in a normal breath under resting conditions.
- **Inspiratory reserve volume (IRV)**: The volume of air that can be forcefully inhaled after a normal inspiration.
- **Expiratory reserve volume (ERV)**: The volume of air that can be forcefully exhaled after a normal expiration.
- **Vital capacity (VC)**: The maximum volume of air that can be exhaled after a maximal forced inspiration. It may be calculated as VC = TV + IRV + ERV
- **Residual volume (RV)**: The volume of air remaining in the lungs after a maximal expiration.

- **Total lung capacity** (**TLC**): The total volume of the lungs, which is calculated

  TLC = TV + IRV + ERV + RV

Table 13.1: Normal Respiratory Volumes

VOLUME	AVERAGE VALUES FOR AN ADULT MALE	AVERAGE VALUES FOR AN ADULT FEMALE
Tidal Volume (TV)	600 ml	500 ml
Inspiratory Reserve Volume (IRV)	3000 ml	1900 ml
Expiratory Reserve Volume (ERV)	1200 ml	800 ml
Vital Capacity (VC)	5300 ml	3200 ml
Residual Volume (RV)	1200 ml	1000 ml
Total Lung Capacity (TLC)	6000 ml	4200 ml

Respiratory volumes are measured with an instrument called a **spirometer**. Some spirometers record air volumes on a moving paper with a recording pen that reacts when a bell within a tank of air or water moves as you breathe into a mouthpiece. Such instruments are called wet spirometers, and they include the Collins spirometer and the Phipps and Bird spirometer. A more convenient, portable, hand-held device measures expiratory volumes only and does not make a recording. The dry hand-held device has a gauge and a mouthpiece for exhaling into, and is often called a Wright spirometer. Both wet and dry types of spirometers are in clinical use and produce similar results.

Exercise 13.2: Measuring Respiratory Volumes by Spirometry

In this exercise, you will use a hand-held spirometer and work with your lab partner to measure respiratory volumes. If you are provided with access to a wet spirometer instead, follow your instructor's directions on its use.

1. Obtain a hand-held spirometer. Prepare it for use by wiping the nozzle with 70% alcohol and inserting a clean, disposable mouthpiece on the nozzle. Work with your lab partner to ensure one of you (the subject) is standing erect during testing and that the gauge of the spirometer is facing upward for reading. Reset the gauge to zero, and you are ready to begin.

Tidal Volume:

2. Check to make sure that the dial on the gauge is reset to zero and that the disposable mouthpiece is in place. Instruct your subject to pinch their nostrils closed, and take two or three normal breaths. Then inhale normally, place the mouthpiece to the lips, and exhale normally into the spirometer. Record the TV value showing on the gauge in the Data Table provided, then reset the gauge to zero each time and repeat the measurement two more times to obtain three values. Calculate the average TV value and record this also. How does the average TV value compare with the normal value presented in **Table 13.1**? _____

_____

Expiratory Reserve Volume:

3. Reset the dial on the spirometer gauge to zero. Instruct your subject to pinch their nostrils and take several normal breaths. Then inhale normally, place the mouthpiece to the lips, and exhale as much air into the spirometer as possible. Record the ERV value showing on the gauge in the Data Table provided, then reset the gauge to zero each time and repeat the measurement two

more times to obtain three values. Calculate the average ERV value and record this also. How does the average ERV value compare with the normal value in **Table 13.1**? _____

Vital Capacity:

4. Use a respiratory nomogram to predict your VC based on your sex and height. Record the value below. Reset the dial on the spirometer gauge to zero. Instruct your subject to pinch their nostrils and take several normal breaths. Then inhale deeply, taking in as much air into the lungs as possible. Quickly place the mouthpiece to the lips, and exhale as much air into the spirometer as possible and as quickly as possible. Record the VC value showing on the gauge in the Data Table provided, then reset the gauge to zero each time and repeat the measurement two more times to obtain three values. Calculate the average VC value and record this also. Predicted VC value from respiratory nomogram _____ How does the average VC value compare with the predicted value from the respiratory nomogram. _____

Inspiratory Reserve Volume:

5. The hand-held spirometer is unable to measure inspiratory reserve volume (IRV), because the measurement would require inhalation and the instrument is not capable of measuring inhaled volumes. However, the IRV can be calculated from the measurements you have obtained previously. From the TV, ERV, and VC values obtained by measurement, determine IRV by performing the calculation:

$$IRV = VC - (TV + ERV)$$

Record your IRV in the Data Table provided for the average measured values.

How does your IRV compare with normal values (**Table 13.1**)? _____

Total Lung Capacity:

6. Use the information you have collected to calculate the total lung capacity (TLC) with the formula below; use the average RV value of 1200 ml in your calculation:

$$TLC = TV + IRV + ERV + RV$$

How does your TLC compare with normal values (**Table 13.1**)? _____

Data Table: Pulmonary Ventilation

Measurement	Test 1	Test 2	Test 3	Average
TV				
ERV				
VC				
IRV (calculated)	X	X	X	
TLC (calculated)	X	X	X	

The Role of Carbon Dioxide in Respiration

As you know, pulmonary ventilation is necessary for oxygen to become available to body cells. Pulmonary ventilation is also necessary for elimination of the waste product of cellular respiration, carbon dioxide, from the blood. If the expiration process of ventilation were to fail, the accumulation of carbon dioxide in the blood would quickly exceed the blood's buffering capability, lowering the blood's pH to toxic levels of acidity.

The body regulates pH levels in the blood through the control of pulmonary ventilation. For example, during exercise, carbon dioxide levels rise due to increased metabolism. Consequently, more hydrogen and bicarbonate ions are produced. The rising levels of hydrogen ions result in a decrease in blood pH. The drop in blood pH triggers chemoreceptors in the aortic arch, carotid bodies, and brain to cause an increase in pulmonary ventilation rate. As a result, the heavier breathing removes more carbon dioxide from the blood through expiration. The process continues until hydrogen ion levels (and pH) in the blood return to normal.

Exercise 13.3: The Effect of Carbon Dioxide on pH

You will demonstrate the influence of carbon dioxide on pH in this exercise by comparing the production of carbon dioxide at rest and after exercise.

Materials: One 100 mL beaker with distilled or deionized water, one 25 mL or 50 mL graduated cylinder, one 50 mL beaker, a sipping straw, and a pH meter (pH paper is not accurate enough for this exercise). Note: Calibrate the pH meters based on directions from your instructor."

1. Identify a subject for your exercise, and instruct your subject to breathe at a normal, resting rhythm for one minute. Count the number of breaths and record the number in the Data Table as breaths per minute at rest.

2. Instruct your subject to take a deep breath, then exhale air through (plug nose) the straw into the beaker of 50 mL water for 30 seconds; it may require several breaths of inhaled air to exhale a total of 30 seconds. Immediately after the exhalations, measure the pH of the water in the beaker, and record the value in the Data Table provided as test pH at rest. Discard the water in the beaker and rinse it thoroughly. What chemical reaction is occurring in the water after exhaling into it? _____

    _____

3. Instruct your subject to run in place, climb steps, or run up and down a nearby stairway for roughly 5 minutes. **Immediately** afterward, count the number of breaths over a one-minute period. Record the result in the Data Table as breaths per minute after exercise.

4. **Immediately** after you have counted the breaths, instruct your subject to take a deep breath and exhale through the straw into the water for 30 seconds. It may require several breaths of inhaled air to exhale a total of 30 seconds. Immediately measure the pH of the water in the beaker, and record the value in the Data Table provided as test pH after exercise. How does this value compare with test pH at rest, and why?

    _____

    _____

5. Explain how a change in carbon dioxide will lead to a change in pH, and how this reaction can affect respiratory rate. _____

_____

_____

Data Table: The effect of carbon dioxide on pH

Activity	Breathing Rate per Minute	Test pH
At rest		
After exercise		

6. **Clean-up:** Rinse beakers and return to green trays to be washed. Straws can be disposed of in garbage.

Exercise 13.4: Rebreathing

Measure normal breathing rate for 1 minute and record: _____

Breathe into a paper bag, make sure both your nose and mouth are covered by the bag. Record breathing rates for each minute until a noticeable change in breathing rate occurs. Record results:

Breathing Rate while breathing into a bag:

1 minute _____

2 minutes _____

3 minutes_____

4 minutes _____

5 minutes _____

What happened to your breathing rate while you were breathing into the bag?

Describe the physiological mechanisms that explain these results.

Exercise 13.5: Hyperventilation

A. Hold your breath as long as possible and carefully measure the length of time you are able to do so. Record result: _____

Next, hyperventilate (inhale and exhale deeply and forcefully) 10 times. After you have completed the hyperventilation, hold your breath as long as you can and carefully measure the length of time of your breath-hold interval.

Record result: _____

How do the two measurements compare?

Describe the physiological mechanisms that explain these results.

B. Once again, measure normal breathing rate and record: _____

Hyperventilate for a period of two minutes as forcefully and deeply as you can. After the two minutes of hyperventilation, lie down on the table and relax. Have your partner measure and record your breathing rate until normal breathing rate resumes.

BREATHING RATE:

1 minute after hyperventilating _____

2 minutes after hyperventilating _____

3 minutes after hyperventilating _____

4 minutes after hyperventilating _____

5 minutes after hyperventilating _____

6 minutes after hyperventilating _____

Describe the physiological mechanisms that explain these results.

CHAPTER REVIEW

Name _____

Instructor _____

1. The trachea is kept open throughout your lifetime due to the presence of:

   a. tracheal cartilages

   b. PSCC epithelium

   c. the trachealis muscle

   d. deep inhalations

2. Tertiary bronchi divide into:

   a. secondary bronchi

   b. bronchioles

   c. alveolar ducts

   d. alveoli

3. The shiny, moist membrane lining the inside wall of the thoracic cavity is called the:

   a. visceral pleura

   b. pericardium

   c. parietal pleura

   d. respiratory membrane

4. The inner lining of the bronchioles and wall of the alveoli are composed of:

   a. PSCC epithelium

   b. simple squamous epithelium

   c. stratified squamous epithelium

   d. thin plates of cartilage

5. The volume of exhaled air that can be forcefully exhaled after a normal exhalation is the
   _____.

   a. tidal volume (TV)

   b. simple squamous epithelium

   c. inspiratory reserve volume (IRV)

   d. vital capacity (VC)

6. Rising levels of carbon dioxide in the bloodstream result in:

   a. rising levels of acidity in the blood

   b. expiratory reserve volume (ERV)

   c. a drop in blood pH

   d. all of the above

7. Do the following factors generally increase (I) or decrease (D) respiratory rate and depth?

   _____ increase in blood pH

   _____ decrease in blood O2

   _____ increase in blood CO2

   _____ decrease in blood pH

APPLYING YOUR NEW KNOWLEDGE

1. Asthma is a very common disease characterized by widespread narrowing of the bronchioles and formation of mucus plugs, producing symptoms of wheezing, shortness of breath, and coughing. It can be caused by the release of chemical mediators during an allergic response. Explain why the narrowing of bronchioles, rather than that of the larger bronchi, is the source of the airflow restriction, and why inhaling beta-2 stimulants of agonists can bring relief during an asthma attack.

2. You are working out at the local gym with a good friend who has recently been diagnosed with asthma. While you are both running on the treadmill side by side, you notice that your friend is beginning to have difficulty with breathing. She assures you that she is OK, so you both continue running. After approximately 10 more minutes, your friend admits that she is wheezing, and having trouble breathing. You offer to get her medication. As you are searching for her medication, you see two different inhalers: Azmacort and Albuterol.

   Since you have taken a Pharmacology class, you recall that Azmacort is an anti-inflammatory drug that reduces mucus production in the airways and Albuterol is a smooth muscle relaxant.]

   Which medication would you choose to bring to your friend and why?

   Why didn't you choose the other medication?

CHAPTER 14

The **digestive system** converts food into a form that the body can use for energy, growth, and repair. The word *digest* is derived from the Latin *digestus*, which means to divide, dissolve, or set in order; the digestive system does all three. When the body digests food, it divides and dissolves it into simpler parts, putting the food parts in order for their distribution to all body cells by way of the bloodstream for powering body functions.

The digestive system is a sequence of organs that extend from the mouth to the anus forming a single continuous tube, the **gastrointestinal (GI) tract** or alimentary canal. The parts of this GI tract perform numerous specialized digestive functions from ingesting food to mixing and propelling food, simplifying food by chemical and mechanical means, absorbing nutrient molecules, and eliminating waste (defecation). Associated with the GI tract are **accessory organs** (salivary glands, liver, pancreas) that support digestion by secreting enzymes and other substances into the GI tract.

The laboratory exercises in this unit correlate to Chapter 23 in your textbook and address the following BIO 232 course objectives:

1. Summarize carbohydrate, lipid, and protein digestion and absorption
2. Compare the anatomy and physiology of accessory digestive organs

PHYSIOLOGY OF THE DIGESTIVE SYSTEM

You have learned that the function of the digestive system is the breakdown of food into nutrient molecules and the absorption of these nutrients into the bloodstream for their transport to metabolizing cells. The breakdown of food into nutrient molecules involves propulsion, mechanical digestion, and most importantly, chemical digestion. Chemical digestion is performed by enzymes that catalyze chemical reactions converting ingested substances, called substrates, into smaller more easily absorbable products.

During chemical digestion, enzymes perform **catabolism**, which is the breakdown of a large macromolecule into smaller products. In the mouth, stomach, and small intestine, this process is performed in order to form products, or nutrients, small enough to be absorbed across the cellular or epithelial lining of the small intestine. For example, starch is a large carbohydrate (polysaccharide) with thousands of sugar subgroups, but it is converted in the mouth to much smaller molecules (disaccharides) containing only two sugar subunits by a carbohydrate-cleaving enzyme called amylase. In the small intestine, the disaccharides are further catabolized by maltase into the simple sugar glucose (a monosaccharide). Proteases are enzymes that break down proteins into their subunits, amino acids, in the stomach and small intestine. Lipids (fats) are digested into their subgroups, glycerol and fatty acids, by lipases after they have been partially simplified by the action of bile. Glucose, amino acids, glycerol, and fatty acids are the nutrient molecules that are ultimately absorbed across the lining of the small intestine into the bloodstream.

The complete physiology of the digestive system involves not only chemical digestion but also hormonal control, nutrient absorption and transport of substances. Our lab activities for digestion, being limited to chemistry experiments, will require you to investigate the chemical digestion of carbohydrates and lipids.

You are a student in a nutrition course required as part of a registered dietitian program. You will be working with your colleagues to complete some experiments that will enhance your understanding of digestion in the digestive tract. Be prepared to answer questions relevant to the experiments.

Exercise 14.1: Chemical Digestion of Carbohydrates

In the mouth, the enzyme salivary amylase begins the chemical digestion of carbohydrates by the catabolism of large starch molecules to a disaccharide known as maltose. In this experiment, you will use amylase to demonstrate this chemical reaction. A common indicator solution, Lugol's solution (IKI), will be used to identify the presence of starch, and Benedict's solution will be used in the assay to identify the presence of the disaccharide sugar, maltose. _Safety precaution: Wear disposable gloves and eye protection when handling hot test tubes. Use a test tube clamp to handle hot test tubes and prevent burns; do not use your gloved fingers._

1. Label six test tubes 1-6 with a permanent black marker.
2. In test tube labeled 1, place 2 mL of 5% starch solution and 2 mL of 5% amylase solution. Cover with parafilm and mix by gently shaking.
3. In test tube labeled 2, place 2 mL of 5% starch solution and 2 mL of distilled water. Cover with parafilm and mix by gently shaking.
4. Incubate test tubes 1 and 2 for one hour in a 37 °C water bath.
5. Remove test tubes 1 and 2 from the water bath.
6. Divide test tube 1 into two equal 2 mL amounts in test tubes labeled 3 and 4. Record the color of each test tube in **Table 14.1**.
7. Divide test tube 2 into two equal 2 mL amounts in test tubes labeled 5 and 6. Record the color of each test tube in **Table 14.1**.
8. To test tubes 3 and 5, add one drop of iodine (Lugol's) solution. Cover with parafilm and mix by gently shaking. Record the color of each test tube in **Table 14.1** (may need to hold test tube up to light).
9. To test tubes 4 and 6 add 2 mL of Benedict's reagent. Cover with parafilm and mix by gently shaking. Record the color of each test tube in **Table 14.1**.
10. Boil test tubes 4 and 6 for 5 minutes. Record the color in **Table 14.1**.
    - A positive test for maltose will be evident by a color change of yellow to red.
    - A negative test for maltose will be evident by no color change.

Table 14.1. Data Table: Carbohydrate Digestion

Test Tube	Color before addition of indicator solution (iodine or Benedict's reagent)	Color after addition of indicator solution (iodine or Benedict's reagent)	Color after Boiling
3			–
5			–
4			
6			

11. **Clean-up:** Empty and rinse all test tubes and beakers and return to green tray to be washed. Flush sink with water.

Questions:

1. Explain any changes in the color in test tubes 3-6 and how those changes relate to enzyme activity.

2. A patient presents with a rare disorder called Zollinger-Ellison Syndrome. The patient has developed tumors in the small intestine that release hormones that stimulate the stomach to synthesize and secrete large amounts of HCL. How would this disorder disrupt normal digestive enzyme functions?

3. Compare your data with that of other lab groups, and record your observations and conclusions: _____

_____

_____

_____

Exercise 14.2: Chemical Digestion of Lipids

In the duodenum, lipids (fats) undergo two phases of digestion. During the first phase, bile produced by the liver emulsifies large fat droplets into smaller droplets, resulting in an increase in the surface area of the lipid droplet. During the second phase of lipid digestion, lipases, lipid-digesting enzymes produced by the pancreas, break down lipid molecules that comprise the small droplets into their subunits, such as fatty acids and glycerol. Pancreatin is extracted from pancreatic juice and contains many enzymes, including lipase. In this exercise, you will use pancreatin and litmus cream to demonstrate the second phase of lipid digestion (litmus cream is a mixture of regular cream [lipid substrate] and indicator agent).

1. Label two test tubes 7 and 8 with a permanent black marker.

2. In test tube labeled 7, add 2 mL of Litmus cream and 2 mL of 5% pancreatin solution. Cover with parafilm wax and mix by gently shaking. Record the color, pH and odor in **Table 14.2**.

3. In test tube labeled 8, add 2 mL of Litmus cream and 2 mL of distilled water. Cover with parafilm wax and mix by gently shaking. Record the color, pH and odor in **Table 14.2**.

4. Incubate test tubes 7 and 8 for 1 hour in a 37 °C water bath.

5. After one hour, remove test tubes 7 and 8. Record the color, pH and odor of each test tube in **Table 14.2**.

Table 14.2. Data Table: Lipid Digestion

	Observations Before Incubation		Observations After Incubation	
	Test Tube 7	Test Tube 8	Test Tube 7	Test Tube 8
Color				
pH				
Odor				

6. **Clean-up:** Empty and rinse all test tubes and beakers and return to green tray to be washed. Flush sink with water.

Questions:

1. Where does emulsification occur in the body?

2. In the body, what substance is responsible for emulsification?

3. What is the purpose of emulsification in the body?

4. Explain any changes in the color, pH and/or odor in test tubes 7 and 8 and how those changes relate to enzyme activity.

5. A patient presents with nausea and RUQ pain that begins after a fatty meal and persists for several hours, periodically the pain will radiate to the right shoulder blade. The patient also complains of indigestion and bloating. Predict one possible disorder that may be causing these symptoms.

   Explain the relationship between the disorder you identified and the symptoms arising after a fatty meal.

6. A patient with a history of chronic pancreatitis now presents with diarrhea and weight loss. Explain the patient's symptoms as they relate to lipid digestion and chronic pancreatitis.

Exercise 14.3: Chemical Digestion of Proteins

Protein digestion begins in the stomach with the enzyme pepsin. Pepsin is formed from pepsinogen, a protein produced by the chief cells of the stomach mucosa. Pepsinogen is converted to pepsin in the presence of HCl. HCl secretion is influenced by gastrin (hormone secreted by G cells of gastric mucosa), ACh (secreted by parasympathetic fibers of the vagus nerves) and histamine (chemical produced by enteroendocrine cells in the lamina propria). In this experiment you will use the enzyme pepsinogen to demonstrate the protein digestion. The action of pepsinogen will be tested in the presence and absence of HCl. A common indicator solution, called Biuret solution, will be used to identify the presence of soluble proteins.

1. Label two test tubes 9 and 10 with a permanent black marker.
2. In test tube labeled 9, add 1ml of raw egg white (albumin), 2 mL of pepsinogen and 2 mL of distilled water. Cover with parafilm and mix by gently shaking. Record color and pH in **Table 14.3**.
3. In test tube labeled 10, add 1 ml of raw egg white (albumin), 2 mL of pepsinogen and 2 mL of HCl. Cover with parafilm wax and mix by shaking gently. Record color and pH in **Table 14.3**.
4. Incubate test tubes 9 and 10 for 1 hour in a 37 °C water bath.
5. After one hour, remove test tubes 9 and 10 from the water bath.
6. Add 2 mL of Biuret reagent to test tube 9 and 10. Cover with parafilm wax and mix by shaking gently. Record the color and pH of each tube in **Table 14.3**.
   - Biuret reagent is a common indicator to measure the presence of soluble proteins. The copper sulfate in Biuret reagent binds with peptide bonds. The larger the protein (the more peptide bonds present) the more interactions between Biuret reagent and the protein. Presence of proteins is indicated by a color change to a shade of purple. The greater the change in color intensity the greater the quantity of large soluble proteins present. If color change is pink rather than violet, this indicates shorter peptides and indicates more digestion has taken place.

Table 14.3. Data Table: Protein Digestion

	Observations Before Incubation		Observations After Incubation	
	Test Tube 9	Test Tube 10	Test Tube 9	Test Tube 10
Color				
pH				

7. **Clean-up:** Empty and rinse all test tubes and beakers and return to green tray to be washed. Flush sink with water.

Questions:

1. Explain any changes in the color and/or pH in test tubes 9 and 10 and how those changes relate to enzyme activity.

2. A patient suffers pancreatic insufficiency as a result of cystic fibrosis. This insufficiency primarily results in the decreased secretion of protease enzymes from the pancreas. Correlate this disorder to the changes in digestive enzyme function.

3. John was not paying attention and accidently placed the 5% starch solution in test tube 9 instead of albumin. After incubation and addition of 2 mL Biuret reagent, there was no color change in the solution. Why didn't the pepsinogen act on the 5% starch solution even though HCL was present? Consider the structure and function of an enzyme in your answer.

CHAPTER REVIEW

Name _____

Instructor _____

1. The digestive organ that is associated with the falciform ligament and is located in the RUQ is the:

   a. liver   c. pancreas
   b. small intestine   d. stomach

2. The dome-shaped holding area for food in the stomach is called the:

   a. duodenum   c. body
   b. fundus   d. pyloric antrum

3. The common bile duct carries _____ from the liver and gallbladder to the duodenum.

   a. pancreatic juice   c. bile
   b. nutrient-rich blood   d. digestive enzymes

4. The stomach mucosa is protected from the potentially damaging effects of hydrochloric acid and pepsin by:

   a. a thick stratified epithelium   c. mucus
   b. buffering agents   d. all of the above

5. The distal segment of the small intestine contains shorter villi, and is called the:

   a. duodenum   c. ileum
   b. jejunum   d. cecum

6. Nutrient absorption is assisted by the presence of:

   a. microvilli   c. villi
   b. plicae circulares   d. all of the above

7. Lipid digestion occurs in two phases. The first phase is necessary to break apart large fat droplets, and is performed by:

   a. lipases   c. proteases
   b. bile   d. Benedict's solution

APPLYING YOUR NEW KNOWLEDGE

1. There are many weight loss products available both by prescription and over the counter. One over the counter product is a drug that disables lipases within the digestive tract. Based on your knowledge of digestive physiology, explain how this product works to promote weight loss.

2. You are working with a nutritionist counseling clients on how to make the best nutritional choices to match their lifestyles. One of your clients is a 32 y/o female; she is 5"6" and weighs 105 lbs. She exercises 5 days a week for 45-60 minutes. Recently she experienced moderate abdominal pain and a continual mild fever. An ultrasound of the upper abdomen revealed gallstones in the GB and cystic duct. A cholecystectomy was performed.

    Keeping in mind this patient's profile, what nutritional plan would you suggest for her?

3. A peptic ulcer is an erosion of the wall of a GI tract organ, usually the stomach (where it is called a gastric ulcer) or the duodenum (where it is called a duodenal ulcer). In severe cases, the ulcer may penetrate all four layers of the organ's wall and cause internal bleeding and inflammation of the peritoneum, known as peritonitis. Using the internet or resources from your school's library, describe the current medical view of the cause of peptic ulcers.

CHAPTER 15

The **urinary system** works every moment of your life to maintain the purity and health of the body's fluids by removing unwanted substances and recycling others. The system's most important organs are the kidneys, which filter gallons of fluids every day. The kidneys remove metabolic wastes, toxins, excess ions, and water that leave the body as urine, while returning needed substances back to the blood; this function is known as **excretion**. In addition to performing excretion, the kidneys also help regulate blood pressure, pH, and red blood cell production in the bone marrow. Because all of these functions are essential for your survival, the kidneys are vital organs; a loss of both kidneys requires medical intervention in order to sustain life. The other organs of the urinary system convey urine to the exterior, and include the ureters, urinary bladder, and urethra.

The laboratory exercises in this unit correlate to Chapter 25 in your textbook and address the following BIO 232 course objectives:

1. Examine the process of urine formation and urine excretion

2. Analyze the role of the urinary and respiratory systems in regulating blood and urine pH
   Dissection of the Mammalian Kidney

Dissection of the mammalian kidney provides you with a hands-on study of kidney anatomy. Because kidney structure is very similar among all mammals, any mammalian specimen serves as a close comparison with the human kidney. The sheep and pig kidneys are the most common type used in the lab, because they can be purchased from a biological supply house in a preserved state. Alternatively, your instructor may provide you with a fresh specimen.

Exercise 15.1: Kidney Dissection

You will dissect a mammalian kidney as an additional study of kidney anatomy in this exercise. _Safety precaution: Use disposable gloves when dissecting . Use great care while handling sharp instruments to avoid injury. Dispose of all discarded tissues properly._

1. Obtain a dissecting tray, dissection instruments, and a preserved or fresh kidney. In the following protocol, refer often to **Figure 15.1**.

2. Wearing disposable gloves, place the kidney on the dissecting tray and examine its exterior. If your specimen is fresh, look for the adrenal gland, which may still be attached by connective tissue fibers to the superior margin (the adrenal glands are usually removed in preserved specimen prior to shipping). Identify the slightly concave surface as the **renal hilum**. Hopefully, part of the **renal artery**, **renal vein**, and **ureter** will be present to observe at the hilum. If present, notice the ureter is smaller in diameter than either blood vessel. Explain why: _____

_____

3. Use a scalpel (or knife) to slice the kidney completely through the frontal plane to separate the kidney into anterior and posterior sections. Try to slice with a single motion, rather than a sawing motion.

4. Observe the interior of the kidney, beginning from the outer surface and working inward. Identify the **renal capsule** as the thin, outermost connective tissue covering, then peel away its edge with tweezers to observe its thin structure. Identify the granular **renal cortex** and the striated **renal medulla**, and notice the triangular **renal pyramids** and the **renal columns** between them, all of which make up the medulla. How many renal pyramids can you identify in your specimen? _____ Identify the **renal papillae** at the apices of the renal pyramids.

5. In a preserved specimen that is injected with colored latex, the **glomeruli** may be visible as red and blue dots of color within the cortex.

6. Observe the **renal pelvis**, and notice that it is a membrane-lined basin. Identify the cup-shaped **major** and **minor calyces** that extend from the pelvis toward the renal pyramids and papillae. Observe the **renal sinus**, recognized by its fatty tissue content, surrounding the renal pelvis within the hilum.

7. **Clean-up:** Store dissected kidneys in plastic bags. Make sure to put your name on the bag and store in green tray with instructor's name. Dispose of any unwanted tissues in gargage. Wash and dry all dissection tools.. Rinse and dry dissection tray. Reline tray with new paper towel.

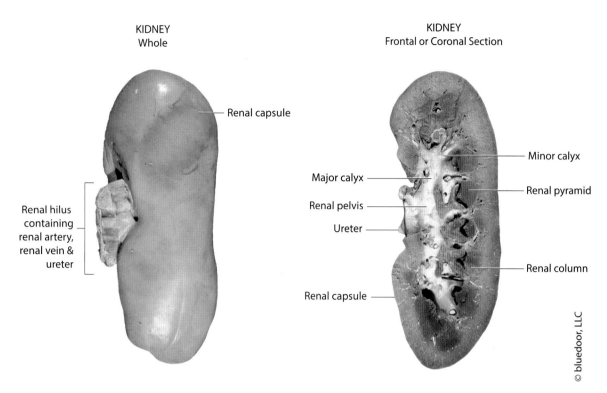

KIDNEY
Whole

KIDNEY
Frontal or Coronal Section

Renal capsule

Renal hilus containing renal artery, renal vein & ureter

Minor calyx

Major calyx

Renal pelvis

Ureter

Renal pyramid

Renal column

Renal capsule

© bluedoor, LLC

Figure 15.1: Photographs of the mammalian kidney. (a) External view of the left pig kidney. (b) Internal view of a frontal section.

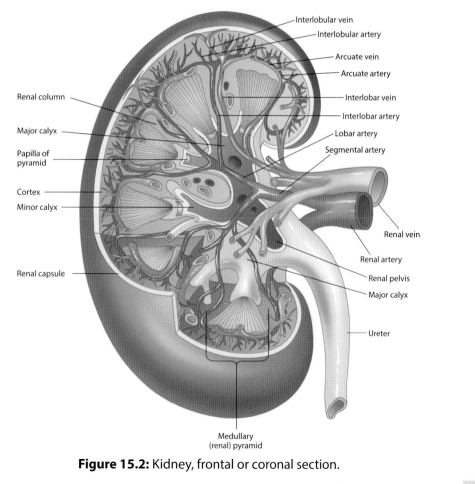

Interlobular vein

Interlobular artery

Arcuate vein

Arcuate artery

Interlobar vein

Interlobar artery

Lobar artery

Segmental artery

Renal column

Major calyx

Papilla of pyramid

Cortex

Minor calyx

Renal capsule

Renal vein

Renal artery

Renal pelvis

Major calyx

Ureter

Medullary (renal) pyramid

© bluedoor, LLC

Figure 15.2: Kidney, frontal or coronal section.

URINALYSIS

In a 24-hour period, the two kidneys filter about 170 liters of fluid (roughly 30 times the total blood volume of the body) through 2 million glomeruli. In a healthy person, this level of activity produces an average of about 1.5 liters of urine output. This enormous level of processing maintains blood composition within relatively narrow limits of nitrogen-containing waste, water content, and pH.

The composition of urine is a reliable measure of the efficiency of the urinary system. In healthy persons, freshly voided urine is usually clear, pale yellow to amber in color, and has a slightly aromatic odor. Any changes in the typical physical characteristics suggests the presence of an abnormality. Thus, the physical characteristics of urine carry information that can provide health professionals with helpful data on a patient's state of health. An analysis of urine composition is commonly known as **urinalysis**.

In a urinalysis, the physical characteristics of urine, including volume, color, turbidity, odor, pH, and specific gravity are examined and compared to normal standards. Healthy urine volume ranges from 1 to 2 liters every 24 hours. Although urine volume is influenced by the amount of water, coffee, tea, soda, and other drinks consumed, a change in volume independent of this factor can indicate an abnormality, such as diabetes insipidus, diabetes mellitus or renal failure. A change from the normal color range from yellow to amber may suggest blood in the urine, which occurs during kidney injury, infection, glomerulonephritis, or tumor. Turbidity refers to the clarity of a liquid. Cloudy urine (increased turbidity) often suggests the presence of bacteria in the urine, a common condition seen in urinary tract infection (UTI). Mineral crystals, pus, or epithelial cells may also contribute to urine cloudiness. The odor of urine is usually slightly aromatic when fresh, and changes to ammonia-like after standing due to the bacterial conversion of urea to ammonia. A strong odor of ammonia suggests abnormal levels of bacteria may be present, providing more evidence of a UTI. Sweet-smelling urine is an indication of glucose in the urine, which may be an indication of diabetes mellitus. The normal pH of urine ranges from 4.6 to 8.0, with an average of 6.0. The broad pH variation is due to diet; high protein diets produce an acidic urine (due to amino acids), and vegetarian diets cause an alkaline pH. A pH beyond normal range indicates acidosis or alkalosis. Specific gravity is the weight of a liquid compared to an equal volume of distilled water. The specific gravity of distilled water is 1.00, because one ml of water weighs one gram; the specific gravity of urine ranges from 1.001 to 1.035. The range tells us whether the urine is dilute, normally the result of drinking lots of water, or concentrated with solutes.

The solutes in normal urine form about 5% of the volume (95% is water), and include electrolytes, urea, creatinine, uric acid, and metabolic end products that result from the breakdown of hormones and other substances.

Table 15.1 provides a summary of abnormal components that may appear in the urine during various diseased states. These abnormal components are revealed by the urinalysis, and their identification in a urine sample aids in the diagnosis of disease.

Table 15.1: Abnormal Components of Urine

ABNORMAL COMPONENT	CONDITION	CAUSE
Glucose	Glycosuria or Glucosuria	Caused by glucose levels in the blood that exceed the renal tubule's ability to reabsorb it. It is a common sign of diabetes mellitus.
Albumin	Albuminuria	Caused by damage to the glomerular filtration membrane, and resulting in the leakage of large quantities of protein, including albumin, into the filtrate.
Red blood cells	Hematuria	Caused by damage to the glomerular filtration membrane, allowing whole cells from the blood to pass into the filtrate.
Hemoglobin	Hemoglobinuria	Caused by the hemolysis of red blood cells within the bloodstream, which releases hemoglobin into plasma that crosses the glomerular filtraton membrane during renal filtration. Diseases that cause red blood cell hemolysis include hemolytic anemia, glomerulonephritis, transfusion reactions, and burns.
Ketone bodies	Ketonuria	While very small levels in the urine are normal, higher levels are caused by abnormalities in metabolism as a result of enzyme deficiencies, starvation, diets extremely low in carbohydrates, or diabetes mellitus.
White blood cells	Pyuria	Caused by inflammation of one or more organs of the urinary system, often as a reaction to infection.
Casts	Casts	A cast consists of aggregated collections of protein, cells, or cell fragments within the nephron or renal tubule, caused by disease and an abnormally low filtration rate, low pH, or high salt concentration of the filtrate.
Bacteria	Bacteriuria	Bacteria in the urine is a sign of a urinary tract infection, or UTI.

Exercise 15.2: Urinalysis

I. Perform a urinalysis (UA) with your own urine sample or an artificial sample of normal urine provided by your instructor by following these steps:

1. Using 50 ml of the urine sample, observe the color and turbidity.
    Record your findings in the data table provided.

2. Using a urinometer or refractometer, measure the specific gravity of your sample. (if using a urinometer, refer to **Figure 15.3**)

3. Use a urine test strip to determine pH and the presence (or lack of) glucose, protein (albumin), red blood cells, and ketone bodies. Dip one unused test strip into the sample. The strips can be read by matching the color changes of your test strip to the color provided by the strip manufacturer. Generally speaking, results for all tests may be read during the second minute after immersion but readings taken after two minutes have passed should be considered inaccurate.

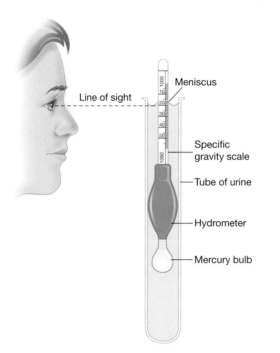

Figure 15.3: Reading the urinometer. The urinometer is read by lining up the lowest margin of the water line, known as the meniscus, with the number on the scale.

Record your results in the data table provided.

II. While working in a free health clinic, your responsibilities include performing UA's on incoming patients. One day was particularly crowded so you decide to try to minimize wait time for the patients. You ask five of the patients to provide urine samples so that you can quickly perform UA's on each. The five patients each provide you with their samples and you label them A – E. (Obtain these samples from your instructor.) Perform a UA on each of these samples and record results in the data table.

4. Once you have recorded all of your data, dispose of test strips in garbage. Rinse all test tubes and urinometers and return to green tray to be washed.

DATA TABLE – UA RESULTS

Test	Normal	Your Sample	Sample A	Sample B	Sample C	Sample D	Sample E
Color	Yellow to Amber						
Turbidity	Clear						
Specific Gravity	1.001-1.035						
pH	4.6-8.0						
Glucose	Absent						
Albumin	Absent						
Ketone Bodies	Absent						
Red Blood Cells	Absent						

Unfortunately, you forgot to label each sample with the patient's name so now you have to figure out which sample belongs with each patient. After obtaining basic vital information of each patient, you perform interviews and note the following:

PATIENT 1:

SEX: F   AGE: 16   HEIGHT: 5'6"   WEIGHT: 86 lbs   BP: 92/54

BODY TEMPERATURE: 98.8° F

PATIENT COMPLAINTS: Lack of energy, thin "lifeless" hair, always feels cold.

PATIENT 2:

SEX: M   AGE: 43   HEIGHT: 6'1"   WEIGHT:185 lbs   BP:140/92

BODY TEMPERATURE: 99.5° F

PATIENT COMPLAINTS: extreme discomfort and pain in back, right side, stomach nausea.

PATIENT 3:

SEX: F   AGE: 75   HEIGHT: 5'4"   WEIGHT: 215 lbs   BP: 190/105

BODY TEMPERATURE: 98.2° F

PATIENT COMPLAINTS: frequent, severe headaches, occasional difficulty with breathing.

PATIENT 4:

SEX: F   AGE: 25   HEIGHT: 5'8"   WEIGHT:133 lbs   BP:130/72

BODY TEMPERATURE: 102° F

PATIENT COMPLAINTS: pain and burning sensation while urinating, frequent urination

PATIENT 5:

SEX: M   AGE: 36   HEIGHT: 5'10"   WEIGHT:280 lbs   BP:140/92

BODY TEMPERATURE: 98.1° F

PATIENT COMPLAINTS: excessive thirst, frequent urination, excessive fatigue, occasional blurred vision.

Based on the results of each UA, which urine sample belongs to each patient?

PATIENT NUMBER	URINE SAMPLE (A – E)
1	
2	
3	
4	
5	

Working with your lab partner(s), choose TWO of the above patients and:

1. Predict a possible diagnosis for the patient.

2. Explain HOW the patient's diagnosis causes the results of their UA.

CHAPTER REVIEW

Name _____

Instructor _____

1. Which of the following functions is NOT performed by the kidneys?

   a. excretion

   b. reabsorption of nutrients

   c. control of pH in body fluids

   d. water balance

2. When dissecting a kidney, cutting through only the renal capsule will expose the:

   a. renal pelvis

   b. renal cortex

   c. renal pyramid

   d. nephrons

3. Newly formed urine flows from the renal papilla into the:

   a. renal pyramid

   b. minor calyx

   c. renal sinus

   d. ureter

4. A renal corpuscle consists of:

   a. the renal cortex and medulla

   b. a glomerular capsule and glomerulus

   c. convoluted tubules and loop of Henle

   d. all of the above

5. Blood enters the glomerulus from the:

   a. afferent arteriole

   b. peritubular capillary

   c. efferent arteriole

   d. arcuate artery

6. A renal pyramid is composed of:

   a. numerous glomerular capsules

   b. interlobular and arcuate vessels

   c. renal tubules and collecting ducts

   d. all of the above

7. The process of _____ occurs with glomeruli, whereas the process of _____ takes place primarily at the renal tubules.

   a. reabsorption; secretion

   b. filtration; reabsorption

   c. filtration; absorption

   d. secretion; reabsorption

8. Dissection of the mammalian kidney revealed the _____, which is a membrane-lined basin within the organ.

   a. renal pyramid

   b. renal sinus

   c. renal pelvis

   d. capsular space

9. A urinalysis is a clinical procedure that determines:

   a. the composition of urine

   b. health status of the patient

   c. properties of a urine sample

   d. all of the above

APPLYING YOUR NEW KNOWLEDGE

1. You have learned in this chapter that a urinary tract infection, or UTI, can be diagnosed with the aid of a urinalysis, which can detect bacteria or white blood cells in the urine. If left untreated, a UTI can cause permanent damage to the kidneys, posing a threat to all functions performed by the urinary system. Explain why the loss of kidney function (to both kidneys) can be lethal.

2. A patient who loses the function of both kidneys can be placed on an artificial dialysis regimen to replace the most essential kidney functions. Which functions are temporarily replaced by artificial dialysis?

3. a. Using **Table 15.1**, identify the diseases that result when the filtration membranes within the kidneys become damaged and are unable to restrict or regulate the movement/filtration of larger substances.

   b. What kinds of disorders cause damage to the filtration membrane?

4. There are many diuretic drugs on the market. One of these drugs, "Furosemide" marketed under the brand name "Lasix" is commonly prescribed to patients for treatment of hypertension, congestive heart failure and edema.

   a. Explain the physiological mechanism by which this drug works to treat these conditions.

   b. How did this drug come by the name Lasix?

   c. Describe one possible side effect of using this drug AND why the drug causes this side effect.

CHAPTER 16

THE REPRODUCTIVE SYSTEM

The reproductive system provides a means of procreation, whereby new individuals are created via the process of sexual reproduction. In the male reproductive system, male gametes are produced and are called spermatozoa, or sperm cells. The male system also sustains and transports the sperm cells, and secretes the hormone testosterone, which regulates sperm cell production and the expression of secondary sexual characteristics. In the female reproductive system, the female gametes are known as ova. The female system supports fertilization, nurtures the developing new life, and gives birth. The female hormones are estrogens and progesterone, which regulate the female cycles and provide for the expression of secondary sexual characteristics.

The laboratory exercises in this unit correlate to Chapter 27 in your textbook and address the following BIO 232 course objectives:

1. Compare the events and hormonal control of the ovarian and menstrual cycles
2. Evaluate spermatogenesis

MALE REPRODUCTIVE SYSTEM

Lab Activity

Examine **Figure 16.1**, a section through the wall of a seminiferous tubule.

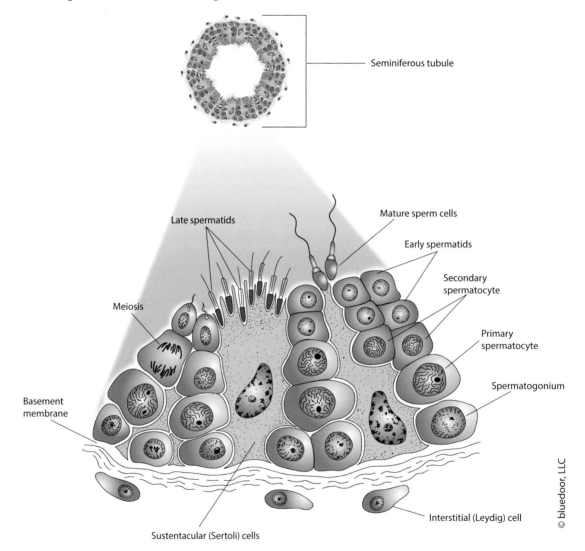

Figure 16.1: Spermatogenesis, as seen from a section through the wall of a seminiferous tubule.

1. Obtain a prepared slide of a section through the testis. Under scanning power, survey the section and located the seminiferous tubules. Switch to low power, and focus on a cluster of seminiferous tubules, then switch to high power, and focus on a single tubule.

2. Using **Figure 16.1** as a guide, identify the following structures in your cross section of a seminiferous tubule: Leydig cells, Sertoil cells, spermatogoium, late spermatids, seminferous tubule.

3. Sketch and label a diagram of your observations in the space provided on page 215.

Discuss with your lab partners and answer the following questions about your observations of spermatogenesis.

1. Is spermatogenesis primarily under hormonal control or nervous system control? Explain your answer.

2. Explain the hormonal pathway for spermatogenesis. Make sure to include the roles of LH, FSH, testosterone, and inhibin in your discussion.

3. What is happening to the size and shape of the cells as they progress through spermatogenesis?

4. Discuss the functions of the sustentacular (Sertoli) cells and the interstitial (Leydig) cells with regard to spermatogenesis?

Examine **Figure 16.2**, a transverse section through the shaft of the penis.

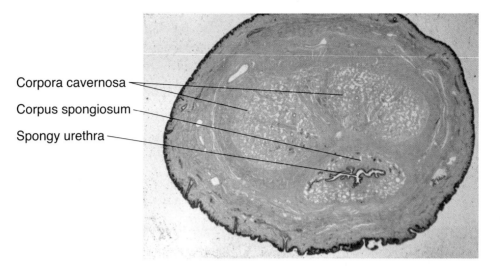

Corpora cavernosa

Corpus spongiosum

Spongy urethra

© bluedoor, LLC

Figure 16.2: Photomicrograph of a transverse section through the shaft of the penis, scanning power (10X).

1. Obtain a prepared slide of a cross section of the penis and view your section using scanning power.

2. Identify the corpora cavernosa, corpus spongiosum and urethra.

3. Sketch and label a diagram of your observations.

4. Discuss with your lab partners and answer the following questions about your observations of the penis.

    a. Is erection under primarily nervous system or hormonal control? Explain your answer.

    b. Erection occurs due to a process called vasocongestion. Describe vasocongestion and how arterial and venous blood flow is altered to achieve vasocongestion in the penis.

    c. Sildenafil citrate (marketed under the name 'Viagra') causes increased blood flow into the penis, thus allowing for erection to occur. Explain the mechanism by which this drug accomplishes this?

FEMALE REPRODUCTIVE SYSTEM

Lab Activity

Examine **Figure 16.3**, a ovary showing follicles in different stages of development.

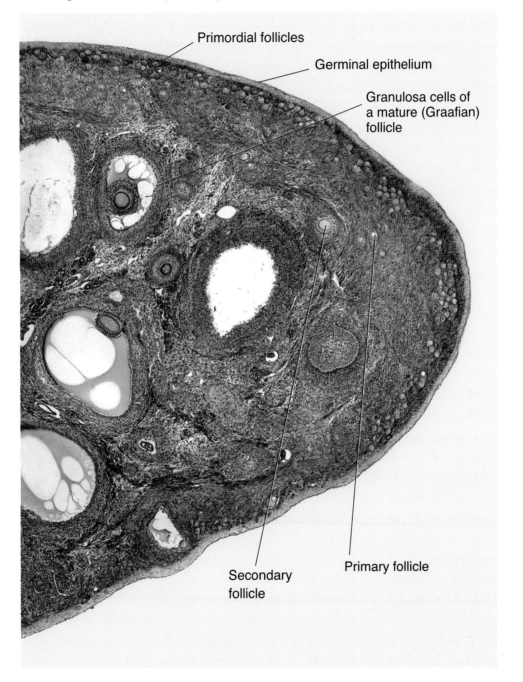

Figure 16.3: Ovary showing follicles in different stages of development.

Examine **Figure 16.4**, a frontal section of the ovary.

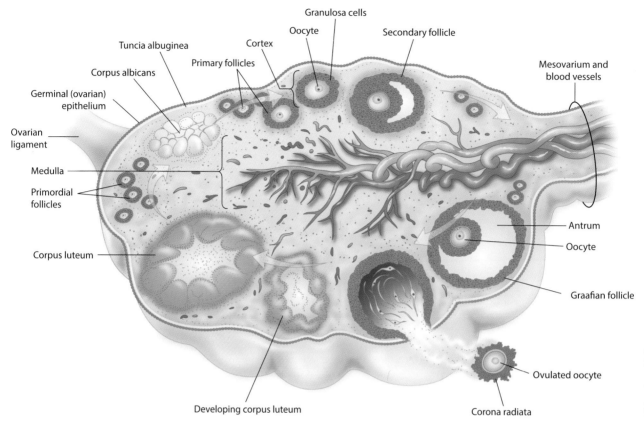

Figure 16.4: The ovary, frontal section.

1. Obtain a prepared slide of a corpus luteum and observe under scanning power. Identify the corpus luteum and ovarian epithelium. The corpus luteum is a large rounded (5mm to 1 cm) structure with "folded" tissue layers.

2. Sketch and label a diagram of your observations.

3. Discuss with your lab group and answer the following questions:

   a. What hormone is primarily responsible for the Graafian follicle rupturing to release the oocyte at ovulation?

   b. What uterine events are occurring when primary follicles are maturing during the follicular phase of ovarian cycle?

   c. What is the dominant ovarian hormone during:

      i. The follicular phase of the ovarian cycle?

      ii. The luteal phase of the ovarian cycle?

   d. Describe a positive feedback mechanism that contributes to ovarian cycling.

   e. If the ovulated oocyte becomes fertilized, what causes ovarian cycling to stop for the duration of the pregnancy?

Examine **Figure 16.5**, a Histology of endometrium, longitudinal section.

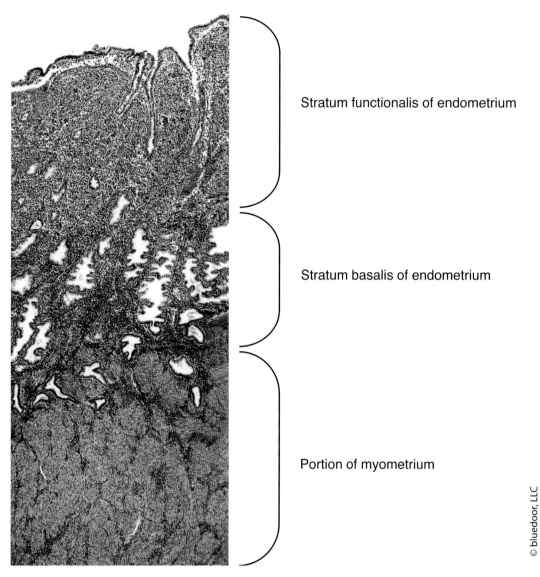

Stratum functionalis of endometrium

Stratum basalis of endometrium

Portion of myometrium

© bluedoor, LLC

Figure 16.5: Histology of endometrium, longitudinal section.

4. Obtain a prepared slide of the uterus and observe it under scanning power.

5. Using low power, identify the stratum functionalis and stratum basalis of the endometrium.
    Use **Figure 16.5** to assist you.

LAB APPLICATIONS

With your lab partner(s), discuss and write out your discussions of the following topics. Be prepared to participate in a class discussion.

Infertility affects one in six married couples of childbearing age in the United States. A couple is considered infertile if they have participated in unprotected intercourse for a year without becoming pregnant. In about 35% of these couples, the problem is in the female reproductive system, in 35% of the couples the problem is related to the male reproductive system, in 20% with both partners, and in 10% of the cases the cause cannot be established. As couples postpone their childbearing until middle age, the rate of infertility has increased.

You are a nurse with Oakton infertility clinic and you are discussing the different possibilities for infertility diagnosis and treatment with a couple -- 45 year old David and 38 year old Anita.

1. You ask Anita for her menstrual dates for the past 6 months and the duration of menstruation for each of her period. If Anita's menstrual flow begins today, _____ (today's class date):

   a. On approximately what date(s) would this person show the highest estrogen levels?_____

   b. On what date(s) would this person most likely have a successful fertilization?_____

   c. When would the LH surge begin?_____

   d. When would this person show highest levels of progesterone?_____

   e. When would this person's progesterone start declining?_____

   f. What is the major cause of the LH surge?_____

   g. What is the cause of the drop in progesterone during the luteal phase?_____

2. In an attempt to gain a better understanding of her hormone levels, Anita and David purchase two different over-the-counter test kits. The two kits purchased are an ovulation test kit and an early pregnancy test kit. One of the kits tests for hCG levels and the other tests for LH levels.

   Which kit tests for which hormone? Explain your rationale. _____

   _____

3. How could David's and Anita's ages impact their fertility? _____

   _____

4. David has previously submitted a semen sample. The following results were obtained (normal values are in parenthesis):

   pH:7.4 (7.2 to 7.8)
   sperm count: 18 million sperm/ml (>20 million/ml)
   volume of semen sample: 4.3 ml (1 to 6ml)
   fructose content: 1000 µg/ml (1200 µg/ml)
   sperm morphology: normal
   motility: 50% with some diagonal movement (60% with good forward movement)
   Length of abstinence prior to sample: 48 hours
   Method of collection: manual

a. Which organ(s) in the male reproductive tract could influence an abnormal pH measurement? Fructose? Sperm morphology? Sperm motility? _____

_____

b. Why is a slightly higher than body pH needed in semen? Why is fructose needed?

_____

c. How might length of abstinence impact the characteristics of the sperm?

_____

d. How could impaired motility affect the ability for Anita to become pregnant?

_____

5. Anita is prescribed Clomid, clomiphene citrate, as a part of the initial treatment for the infertility. Clomid stimulates FSH levels to increase the likelihood for ovulation. Why would an increase in FSH lead to an increased likelihood for ovulation to occur? Explain your answer.

6. Amenorrhea is the absence of menstruation and is often seen in young female athletes. It is thought that low levels of the hormone leptin may be a contributing factor to causing amenorrhea.

a. Why would leptin levels be low in female athletes?

b. Explain the physiological mechanism that would explain how low leptin levels might cause amenorrhea.

c. Why might athletes with amenorrhea show signs of premature osteoporosis?

CHAPTER REVIEW

Name _____

Instructor _____

1. The dartos muscle, cremaster muscle, and tunica albuginea are associated with the:
   - a. female reproductive system
   - b. testes
   - c. male reproductive system
   - d. ovaries

2. Spermatogenesis is localized within the:
   - a. ovaries
   - b. seminiferous tubules
   - c. rete testis
   - d. epididymis

3. From efferent ducts, sperm flows into the:
   - a. ductus deferens
   - b. rete testis
   - c. epididymis
   - d. seminiferous tubules

4. The spermatic cord contains the:
   - a. seminiferous tubules
   - b. ductus deferens
   - c. seminal vesicles
   - d. ejaculatory duct

5. The structure that receives the secondary oocyte after ovulation is the:
   - a. infundibulum
   - b. vesicular follicle
   - c. isthmus of uterine tube
   - d. germinal epithelium

6. The fundus, body, and cervix are the parts of the:
   - a. ovaries
   - b. uterus
   - c. uterine tube
   - d. vagina

7. The mature follicle that contains a secondary oocyte and is ready for ovulation is known as the:
   - a. primordial follicle
   - b. Graafian follicle
   - c. secondary follicle
   - d. uterine follicle

8. The secretory phase of the endometrium is characterized by:
   - a. the abundance of smooth muscle
   - b. the growth of glands and capillaries
   - c. the breakdown of tissue
   - d. the presence of an embryo

9. The uterus of the cat or fetal pig:
   - a. is identical to that of the human
   - b. lacks a cervix
   - c. includes two horns
   - d. is not normally present

APPLYING YOUR NEW KNOWLEDGE

1. It is recommended that males undergo a digital rectal examination (DRE) once each year after age forty. The procedure involves a brief visit to a health specialist who inserts a finger into the rectum to palpate the rectal wall adjacent to the prostate gland. From the information you have learned about the male reproductive system, explain the diseases a DRE may potentially reveal.

2. Endometriosis, a condition in which portions of endometrial tissue spread to surfaces outside of the uterus in the pelvic cavity, is an increasingly common finding among premenopausal women. Given the information you have learned about the female reproductive system, explain the monthly consequences of endometriosis.

3. A friend of yours, a 35-year-old male air traffic controller complains to you that he is unable to consistently achieve erection. He believes that the high stress level he experiences with his career is causing his testosterone levels to be below normal, therefore preventing an erection from occurring. Haven taken a Human Anatomy and Physiology class, how might you explain to your friend what the more likely cause of his problem is?

GENERAL

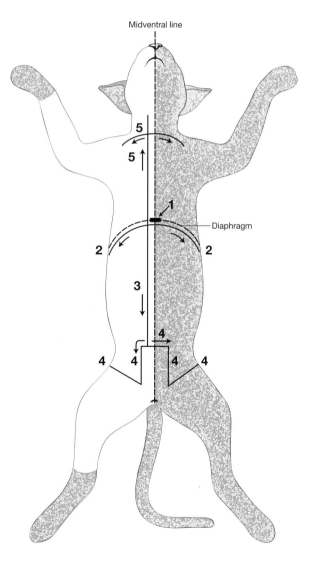

Midventral line

Diaphragm

Figure 1: Cutting guide for exposing body cavities, cat.

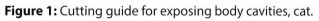

© bluedoor, LLC.

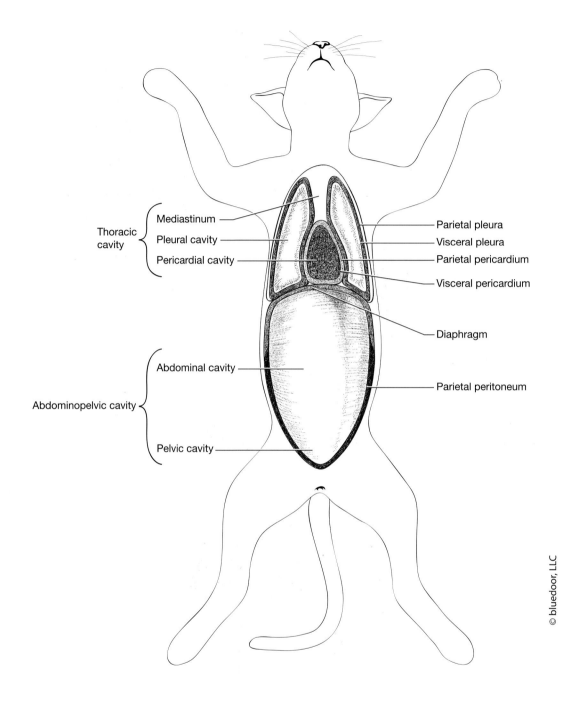

Thoracic cavity
- Mediastinum
- Pleural cavity
- Pericardial cavity

Parietal pleura
Visceral pleura
Parietal pericardium
Visceral pericardium

Diaphragm

Abdominopelvic cavity
- Abdominal cavity
- Pelvic cavity

Parietal peritoneum

Figure 2: Body cavities, cat.

MUSCLES

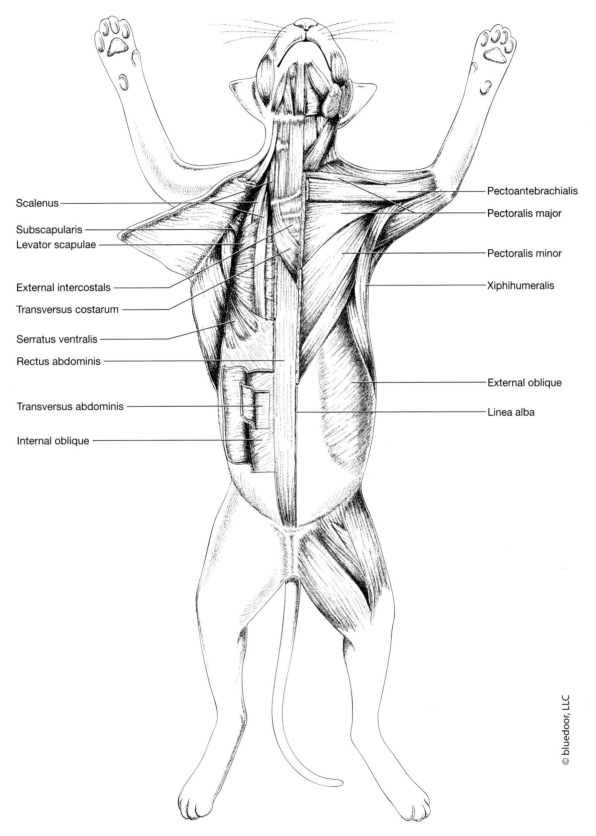

Scalenus

Subscapularis

Levator scapulae

External intercostals

Transversus costarum

Serratus ventralis

Rectus abdominis

Transversus abdominis

Internal oblique

Pectoantebrachialis

Pectoralis major

Pectoralis minor

Xiphihumeralis

External oblique

Linea alba

Figure 3: Ventral muscles, cat.

External oblique   Internal oblique   Transverse abdominis

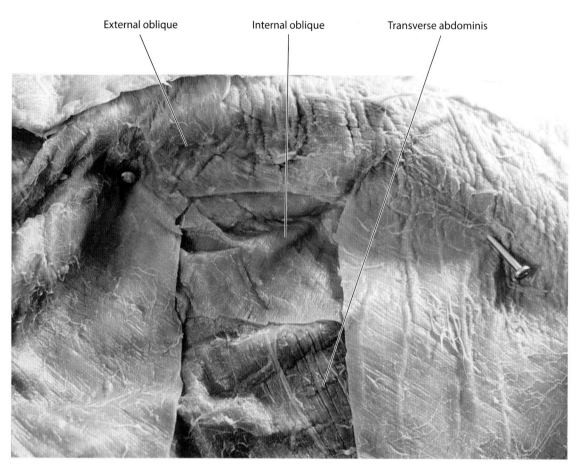

© bluedoor, LLC

Figure 4: Muscles of the abdominal wall, ventral view, cat.

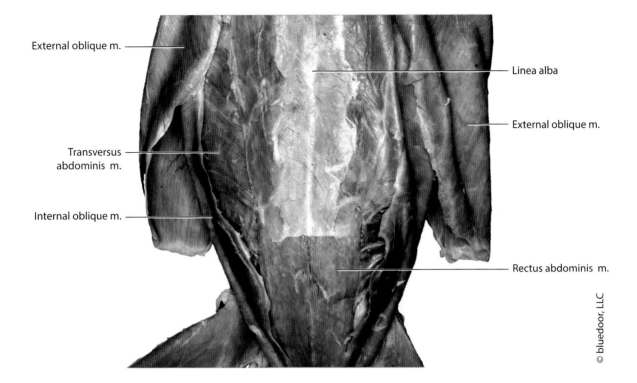

External oblique m.

Linea alba

Transversus abdominis m.

External oblique m.

Internal oblique m.

Rectus abdominis m.

© bluedoor, LLC

Figure 5: Muscles of abdominal wall, ventral view, cat.

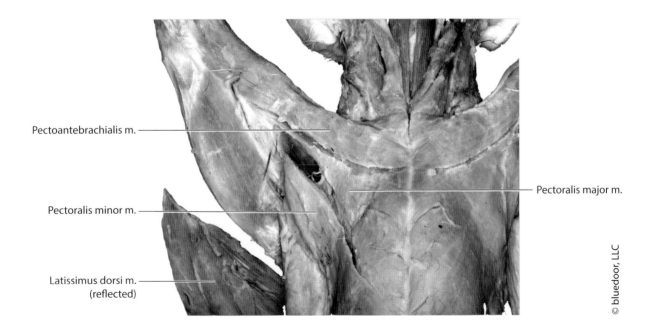

Pectoantebrachialis m.

Pectoralis major m.

Pectoralis minor m.

Latissimus dorsi m. (reflected)

© bluedoor, LLC

Figure 6: Muscles of shoulder, superficial, ventral view, cat.

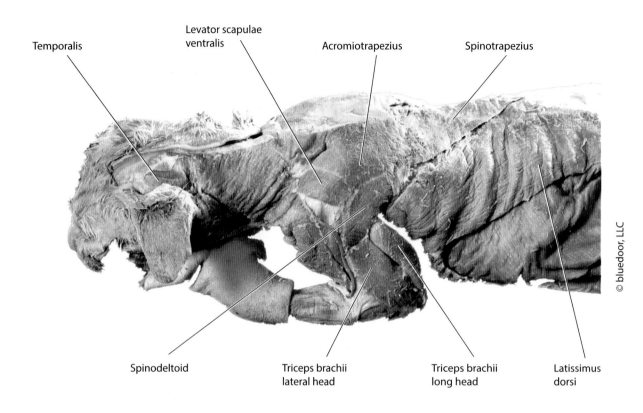

Temporalis

Levator scapulae ventralis

Acromiotrapezius

Spinotrapezius

© bluedoor, LLC

Spinodeltoid

Triceps brachii lateral head

Triceps brachii long head

Latissimus dorsi

Figure 7: Muscles of the neck and shoulder, lateral view, cat.

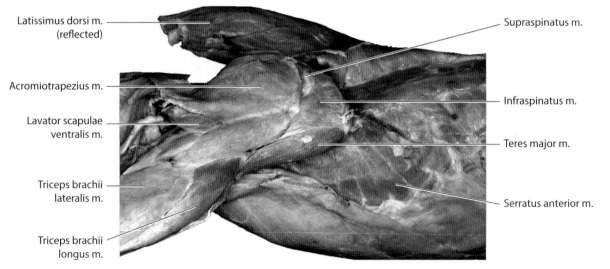

Latissimus dorsi m. (reflected)

Acromiotrapezius m.

Lavator scapulae ventralis m.

Triceps brachii lateralis m.

Triceps brachii longus m.

Supraspinatus m.

Infraspinatus m.

Teres major m.

Serratus anterior m.

© bluedoor, LLC

Figure 8: Muscles of upper back, shoulder, and thorax, lateral view, cat.

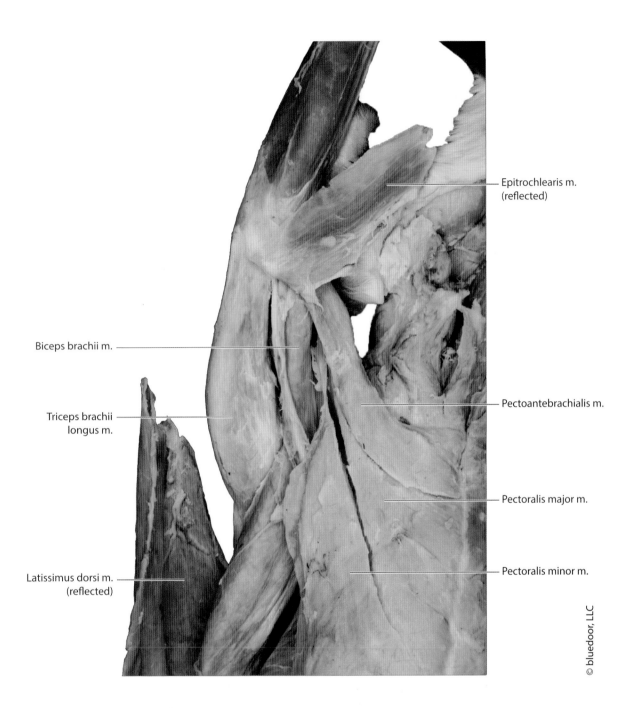

Epitrochlearis m. (reflected)

Biceps brachii m.

Triceps brachii longus m.

Latissimus dorsi m. (reflected)

Pectoantebrachialis m.

Pectoralis major m.

Pectoralis minor m.

© bluedoor, LLC

Figure 9: Muscles of shoulder and brachium, deep, ventral view, cat.

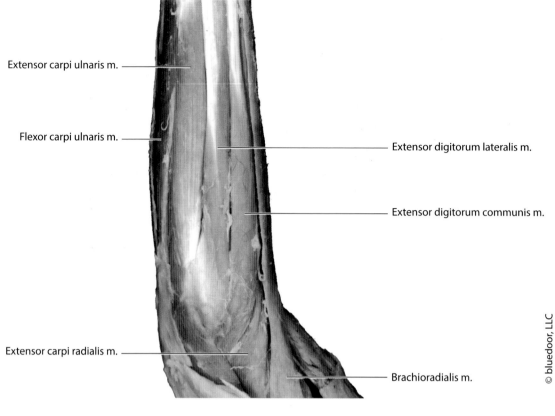

Extensor carpi ulnaris m.

Flexor carpi ulnaris m.

Extensor digitorum lateralis m.

Extensor digitorum communis m.

Extensor carpi radialis m.

Brachioradialis m.

© bluedoor, LLC

Figure 10: Muscles of antebrachium, lateral view, cat.

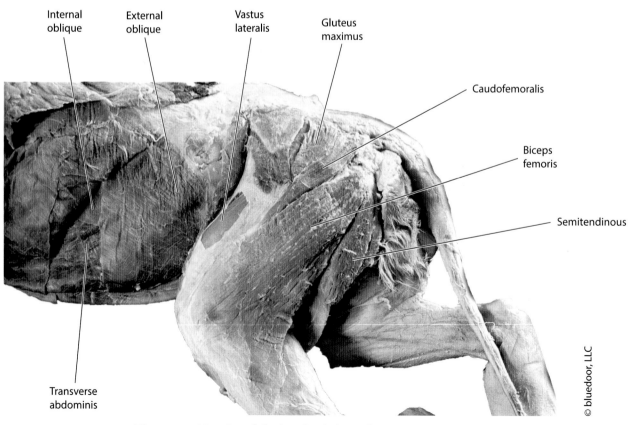

Internal oblique

External oblique

Vastus lateralis

Gluteus maximus

Caudofemoralis

Biceps femoris

Semitendinous

Transverse abdominis

© bluedoor, LLC

Figure 11: Muscles of the hindlimb, lateral view, cat.

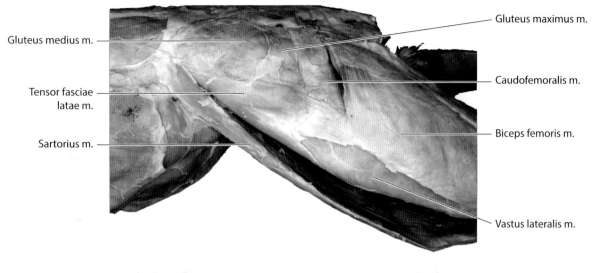

Gluteus medius m.

Tensor fasciae latae m.

Sartorius m.

Gluteus maximus m.

Caudofemoralis m.

Biceps femoris m.

Vastus lateralis m.

© bluedoor, LLC

Figure 12: Muscles of thigh, superficial, lateral view, cat.

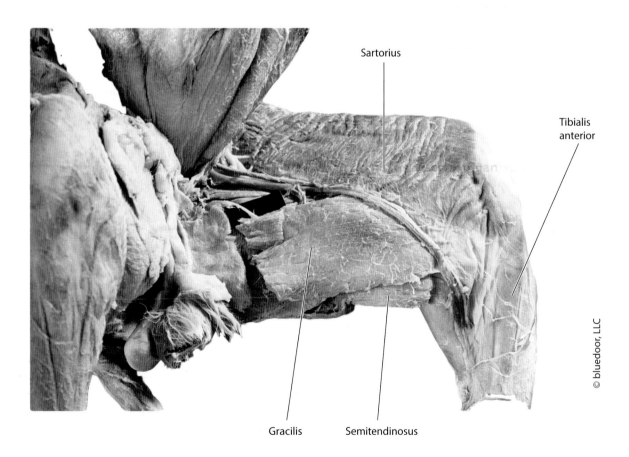

Sartorius

Tibialis anterior

Gracilis

Semitendinosus

© bluedoor, LLC

Figure 13: Muscles of the thigh, medial view, cat.

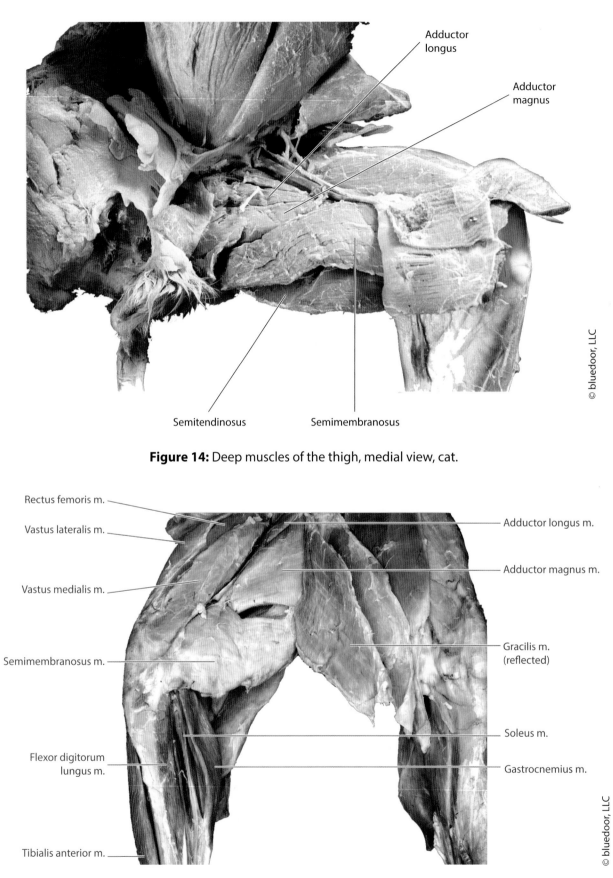

Adductor
longus

Adductor
magnus

Semitendinosus   Semimembranosus

© bluedoor, LLC

Figure 14: Deep muscles of the thigh, medial view, cat.

Rectus femoris m.

Vastus lateralis m.

Vastus medialis m.

Semimembranosus m.

Flexor digitorum
lungus m.

Tibialis anterior m.

Adductor longus m.

Adductor magnus m.

Gracilis m.
(reflected)

Soleus m.

Gastrocnemius m.

© bluedoor, LLC

Figure 15: Muscles of hindlimb, medial view, cat.

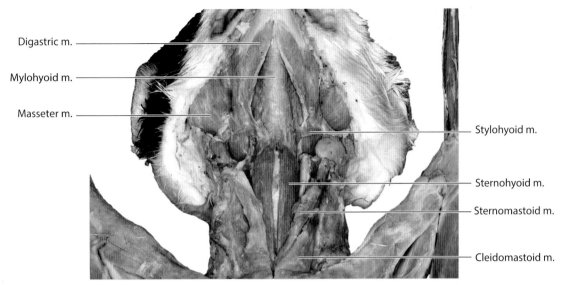

Digastric m.

Mylohyoid m.

Masseter m.

Stylohyoid m.

Sternohyoid m.

Sternomastoid m.

Cleidomastoid m.

© bluedoor, LLC

Figure 16: Muscles of head and neck, superficial, ventral view, cat.

BLOOD VESSELS

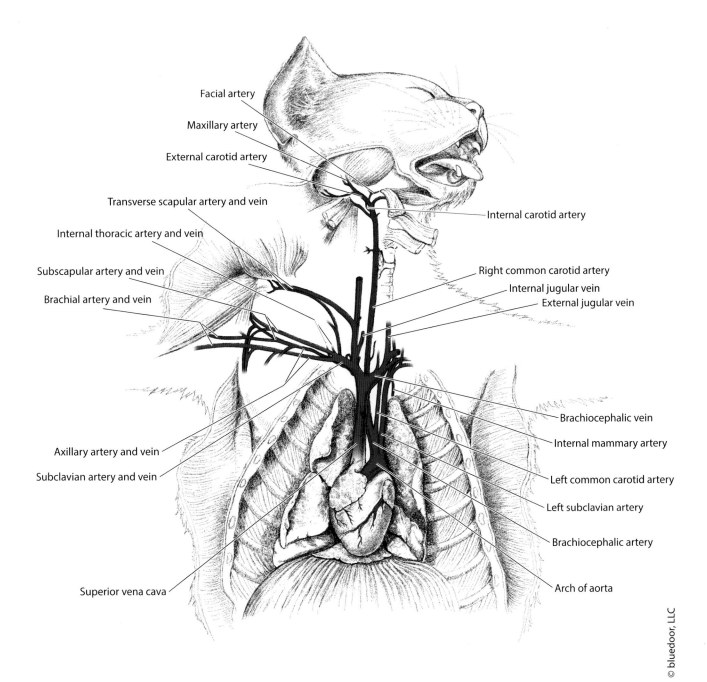

Facial artery

Maxillary artery

External carotid artery

Transverse scapular artery and vein

Internal thoracic artery and vein

Subscapular artery and vein

Brachial artery and vein

Internal carotid artery

Right common carotid artery

Internal jugular vein

External jugular vein

Brachiocephalic vein

Internal mammary artery

Left common carotid artery

Left subclavian artery

Brachiocephalic artery

Axillary artery and vein

Subclavian artery and vein

Arch of aorta

Superior vena cava

© bluedoor, LLC

Figure 17: Blood vessels of the cat, cranial to the heart.

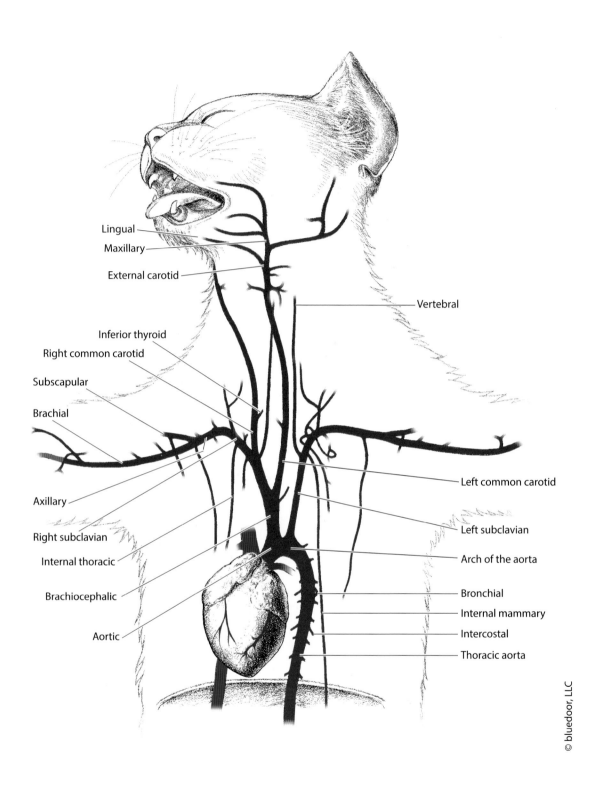

Lingual

Maxillary

External carotid

Vertebral

Inferior thyroid

Right common carotid

Subscapular

Brachial

Left common carotid

Axillary

Left subclavian

Right subclavian

Arch of the aorta

Internal thoracic

Bronchial

Brachiocephalic

Internal mammary

Intercostal

Aortic

Thoracic aorta

© bluedoor, LLC

Figure 18: Arteries of the cat, cranial to the heart.

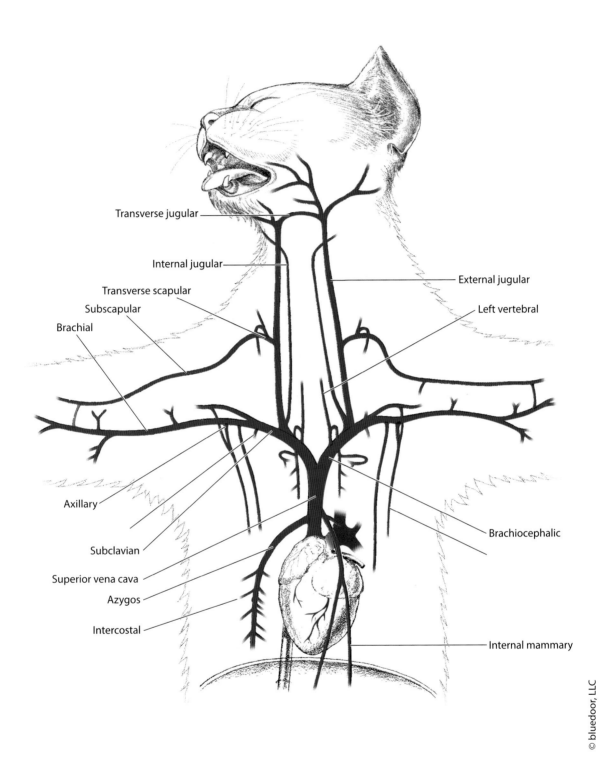

Transverse jugular

Internal jugular

Transverse scapular

Subscapular

Brachial

External jugular

Left vertebral

Axillary

Subclavian

Superior vena cava

Azygos

Intercostal

Brachiocephalic

Internal mammary

Figure 19: Veins of the cat, cranial to the heart.

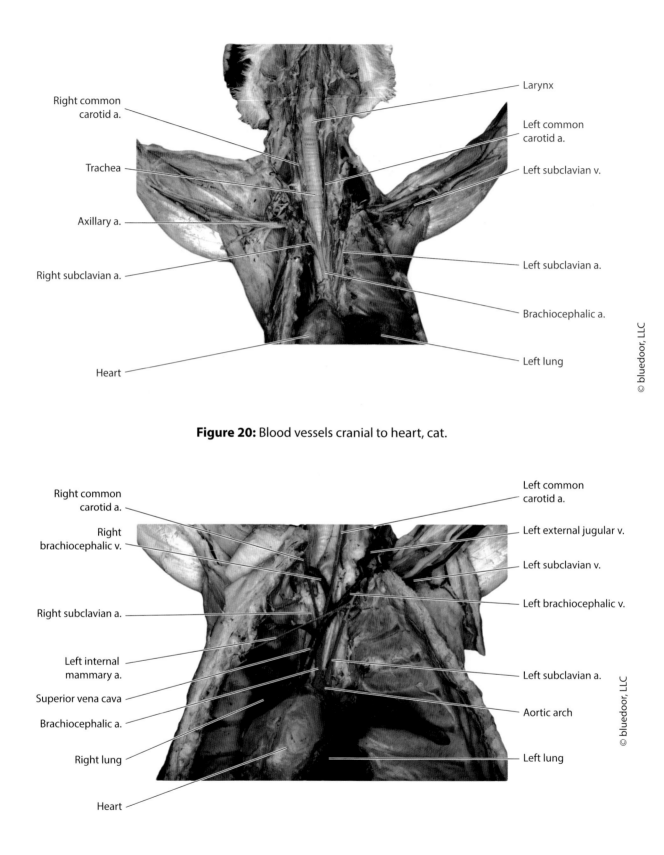

Figure 20: Blood vessels cranial to heart, cat.

Right common carotid a.

Trachea

Axillary a.

Right subclavian a.

Heart

Larynx

Left common carotid a.

Left subclavian v.

Left subclavian a.

Brachiocephalic a.

Left lung

© bluedoor, LLC

Figure 21: Blood vessels of thoracic cavity, cat.

Right common carotid a.

Right brachiocephalic v.

Right subclavian a.

Left internal mammary a.

Superior vena cava

Brachiocephalic a.

Right lung

Heart

Left common carotid a.

Left external jugular v.

Left subclavian v.

Left brachiocephalic v.

Left subclavian a.

Aortic arch

Left lung

© bluedoor, LLC

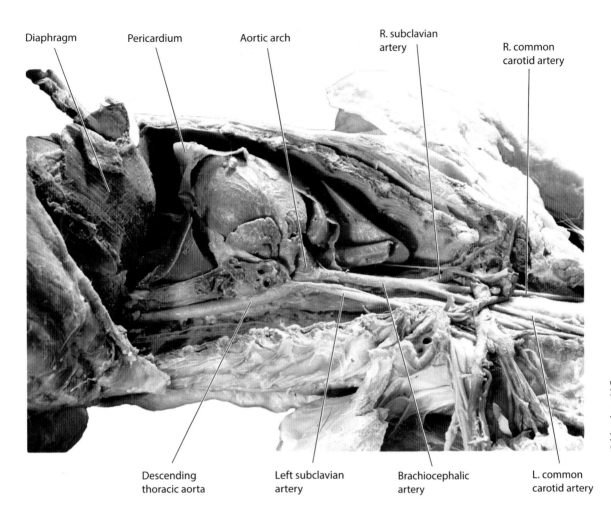

Diaphragm Pericardium Aortic arch R. subclavian artery R. common carotid artery

Descending thoracic aorta Left subclavian artery Brachiocephalic artery L. common carotid artery

© bluedoor, LLC

Figure 22: Blood vessels of thoracic cavity, cat.

Superior vena
cava

R. brachiocephalic
vein

R. common
carotid artery

L. common
carotid artery

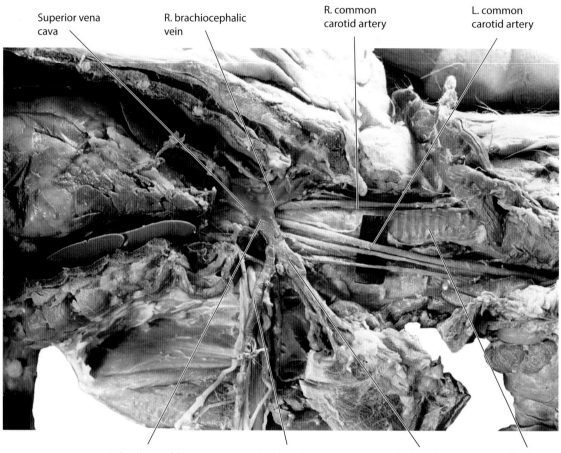

L. brachiocephalic
vein

L. subclavian
vein

External
jugular vein

Trachea

© bluedoor, LLC

Figure 23: Blood vessels of the neck and axilla, cat.

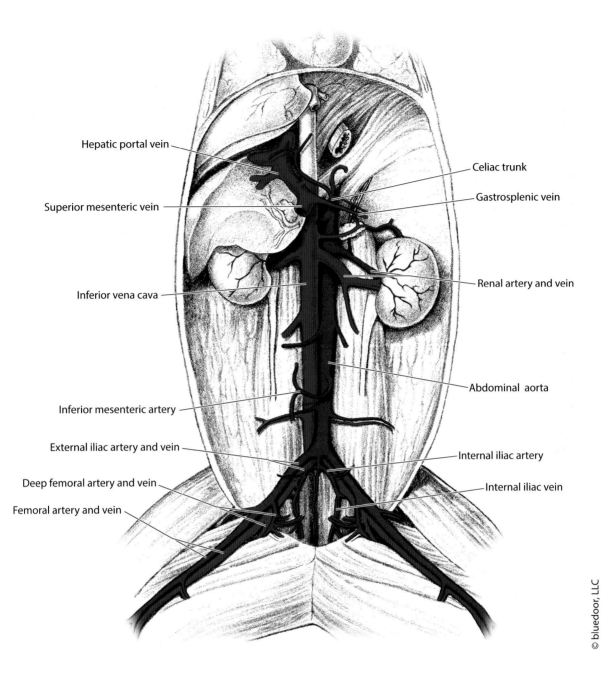

Hepatic portal vein

Superior mesenteric vein

Inferior vena cava

Inferior mesenteric artery

External iliac artery and vein

Deep femoral artery and vein

Femoral artery and vein

Celiac trunk

Gastrosplenic vein

Renal artery and vein

Abdominal aorta

Internal iliac artery

Internal iliac vein

Figure 24: Blood vessels of the cat, caudal to the heart.

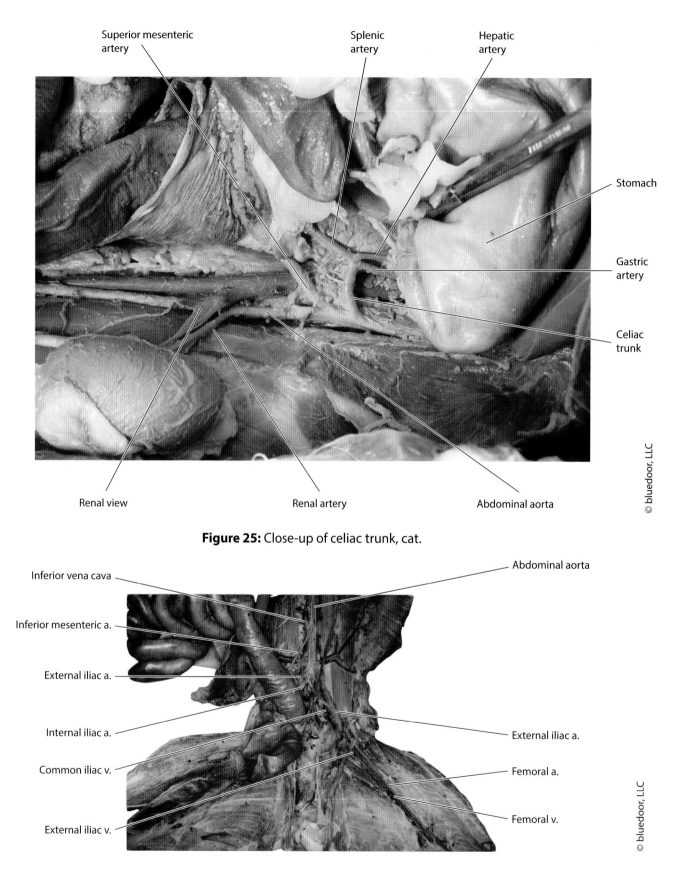

Superior mesenteric artery

Splenic artery

Hepatic artery

Stomach

Gastric artery

Celiac trunk

Renal view

Renal artery

Abdominal aorta

© bluedoor, LLC

Figure 25: Close-up of celiac trunk, cat.

Inferior vena cava

Abdominal aorta

Inferior mesenteric a.

External iliac a.

Internal iliac a.

External iliac a.

Common iliac v.

Femoral a.

External iliac v.

Femoral v.

© bluedoor, LLC

Figure 26: Blood vessels of abdomen and thigh, cat.

RESPIRATORY SYSTEM

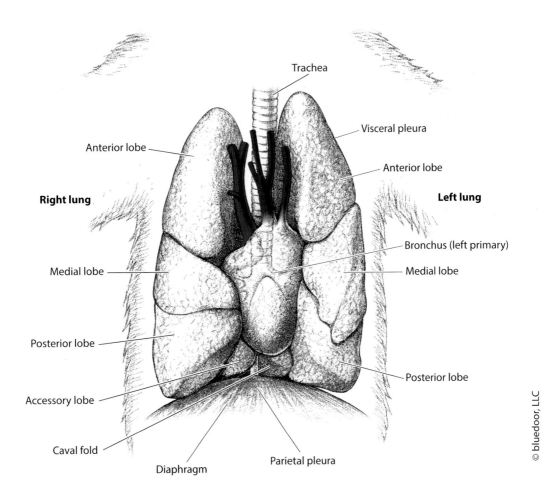

Trachea

Visceral pleura

Anterior lobe

Anterior lobe

Right lung

Left lung

Bronchus (left primary)

Medial lobe

Medial lobe

Posterior lobe

Posterior lobe

Accessory lobe

Caval fold

Diaphragm

Parietal pleura

© bluedoor, LLC

Figure 27: Lungs, external features, ventral view, cat.

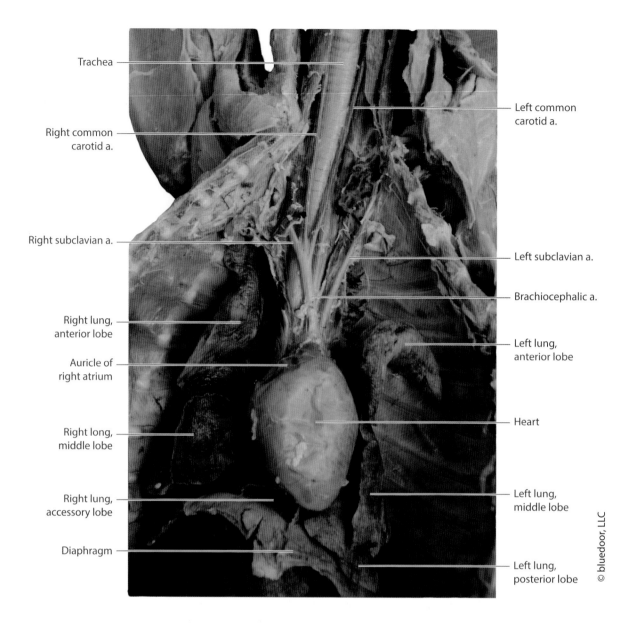

Trachea

Right common
carotid a.

Right subclavian a.

Right lung,
anterior lobe

Auricle of
right atrium

Right long,
middle lobe

Right lung,
accessory lobe

Diaphragm

Left common
carotid a.

Left subclavian a.

Brachiocephalic a.

Left lung,
anterior lobe

Heart

Left lung,
middle lobe

Left lung,
posterior lobe

© bluedoor, LLC

Figure 28: Organs of thoracic cavity, cat.

DIGESTIVE SYSTEM

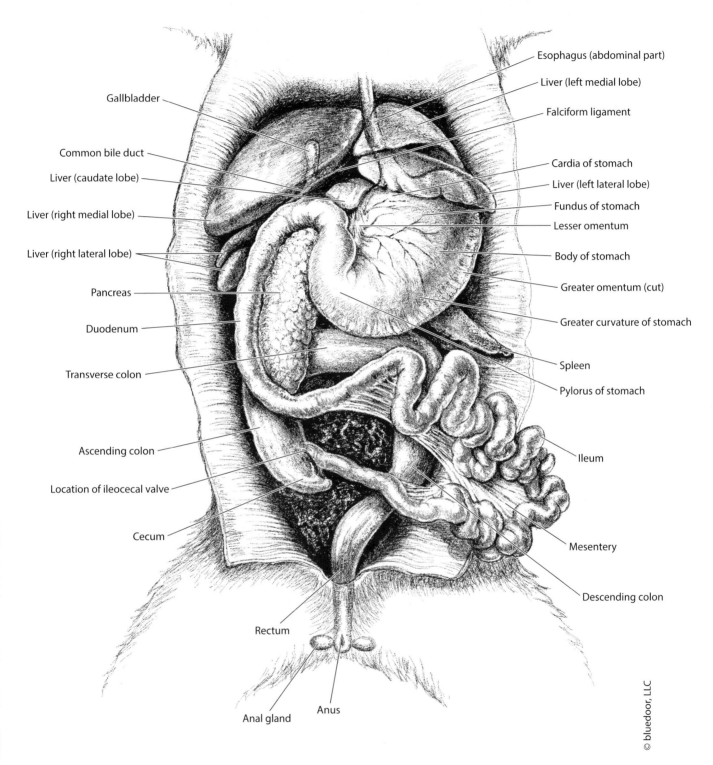

Gallbladder

Common bile duct

Liver (caudate lobe)

Liver (right medial lobe)

Liver (right lateral lobe)

Pancreas

Duodenum

Transverse colon

Ascending colon

Location of ileocecal valve

Cecum

Rectum

Anal gland

Anus

Esophagus (abdominal part)

Liver (left medial lobe)

Falciform ligament

Cardia of stomach

Liver (left lateral lobe)

Fundus of stomach

Lesser omentum

Body of stomach

Greater omentum (cut)

Greater curvature of stomach

Spleen

Pylorus of stomach

Ileum

Mesentery

Descending colon

Figure 29: Abdominopelvic cavity organs, cat.

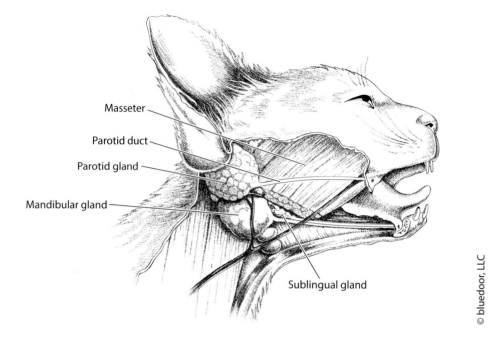

Masseter

Parotid duct

Parotid gland

Mandibular gland

Sublingual gland

© bluedoor, LLC

Figure 30: Salivary glands, cat.

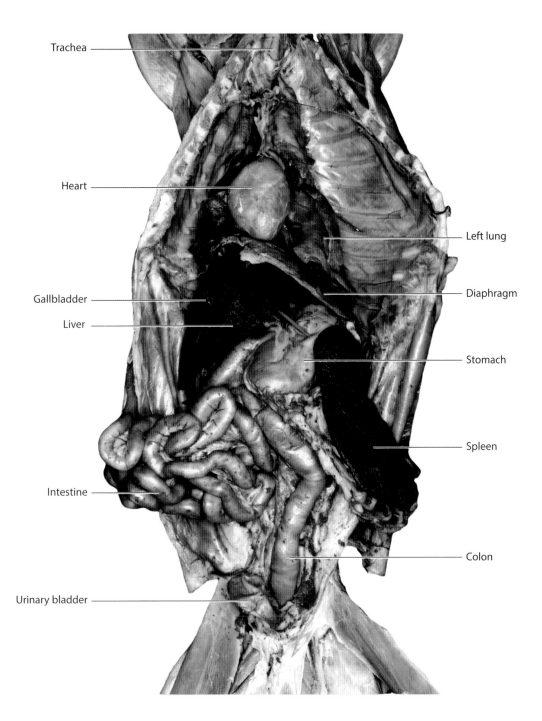

Trachea

Heart

Gallbladder

Liver

Intestine

Urinary bladder

Left lung

Diaphragm

Stomach

Spleen

Colon

Figure 31: Internal organs of cat.

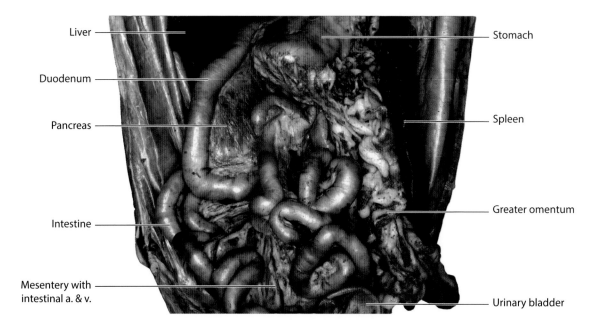

Liver

Duodenum

Pancreas

Intestine

Mesentery with
intestinal a. & v.

Stomach

Spleen

Greater omentum

Urinary bladder

Figure 32: Abdominal cavity, cat.

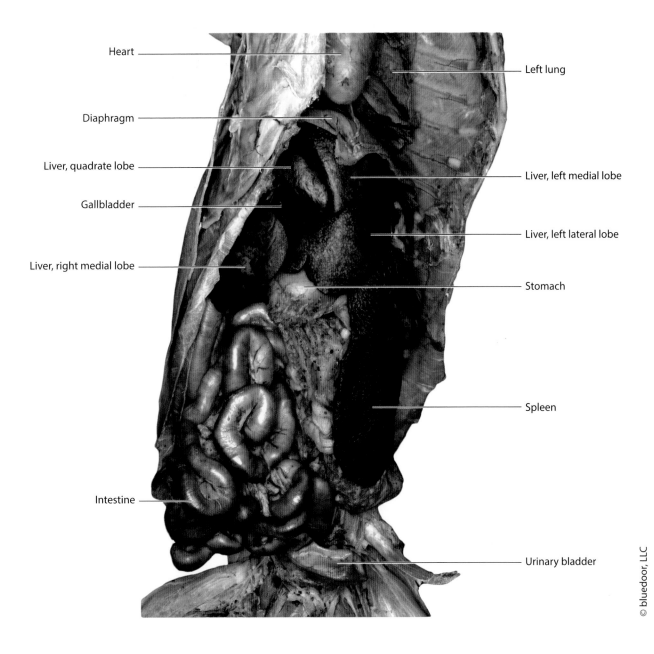

Heart

Diaphragm

Liver, quadrate lobe

Gallbladder

Liver, right medial lobe

Intestine

Left lung

Liver, left medial lobe

Liver, left lateral lobe

Stomach

Spleen

Urinary bladder

© bluedoor, LLC

Figure 33: Abdominopelvic cavity, superficial structures, cat.

UROGENITAL SYSTEM

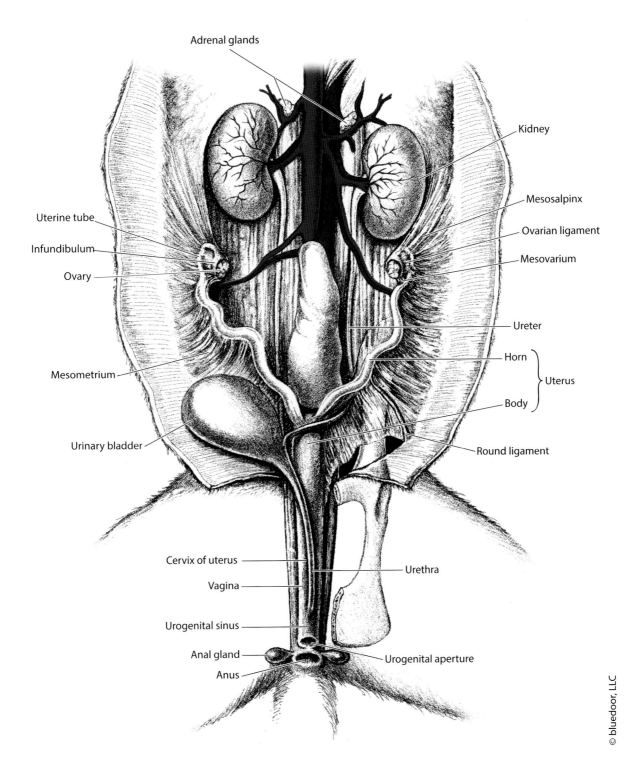

Adrenal glands

Kidney

Mesosalpinx

Ovarian ligament

Uterine tube

Mesovarium

Infundibulum

Ovary

Ureter

Horn ⎫
       ⎬ Uterus
Body ⎭

Mesometrium

Urinary bladder

Round ligament

Cervix of uterus

Urethra

Vagina

Urogenital sinus

Anal gland

Urogenital aperture

Anus

© bluedoor, LLC

Figure 34: Female urogenital system, cat.

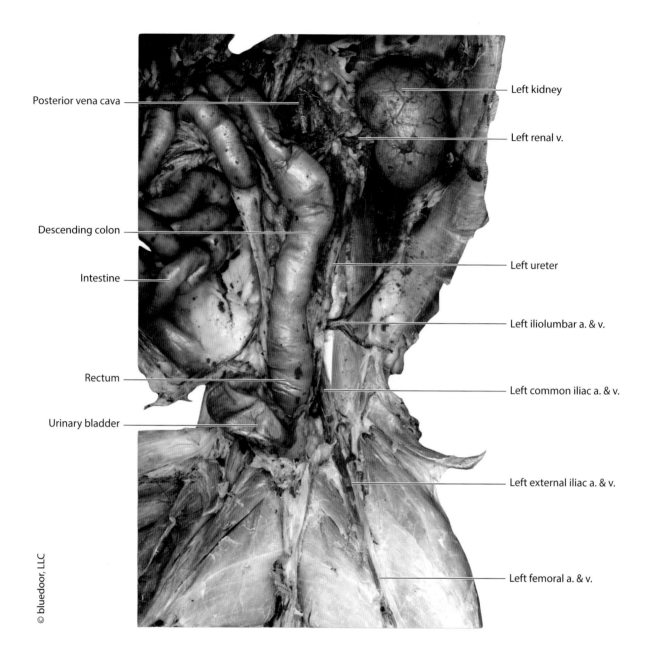

Posterior vena cava

Descending colon

Intestine

Rectum

Urinary bladder

Left kidney

Left renal v.

Left ureter

Left iliolumbar a. & v.

Left common iliac a. & v.

Left external iliac a. & v.

Left femoral a. & v.

© bluedoor, LLC

Figure 35: Abdominopelvic cavity, deep structures, cat.

Descending
colon

Ovary

Uterine
tube

Uterine
horns

Body of
uterus

Figure 36: Female reproductive system, cat.

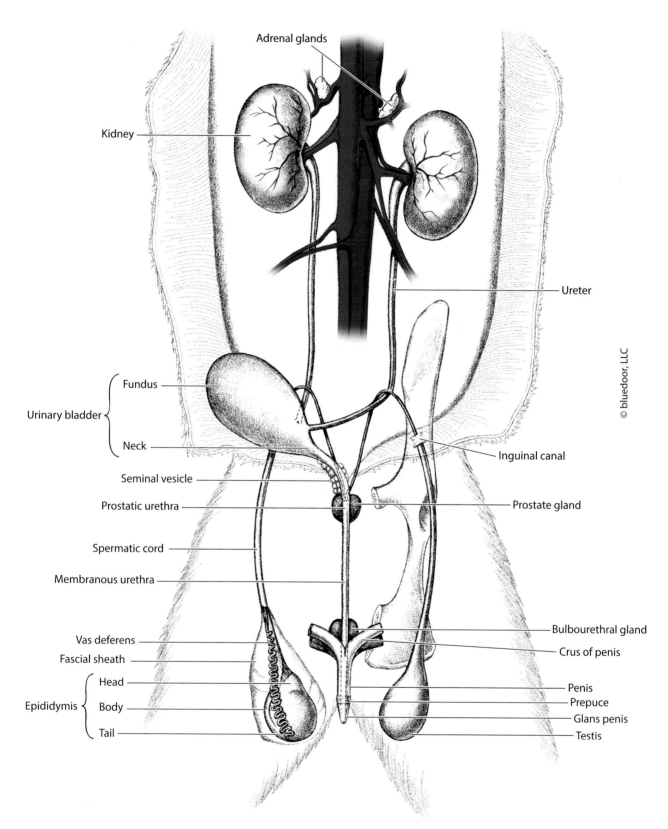

Adrenal glands

Kidney

Ureter

Urinary bladder

Fundus

Neck

Inguinal canal

Seminal vesicle

Prostatic urethra

Prostate gland

Spermatic cord

Membranous urethra

Vas deferens

Fascial sheath

Bulbourethral gland

Crus of penis

Epididymis

Head

Body

Tail

Penis

Prepuce

Glans penis

Testis

© bluedoor, LLC

Figure 37: Male reproductive system, cat.

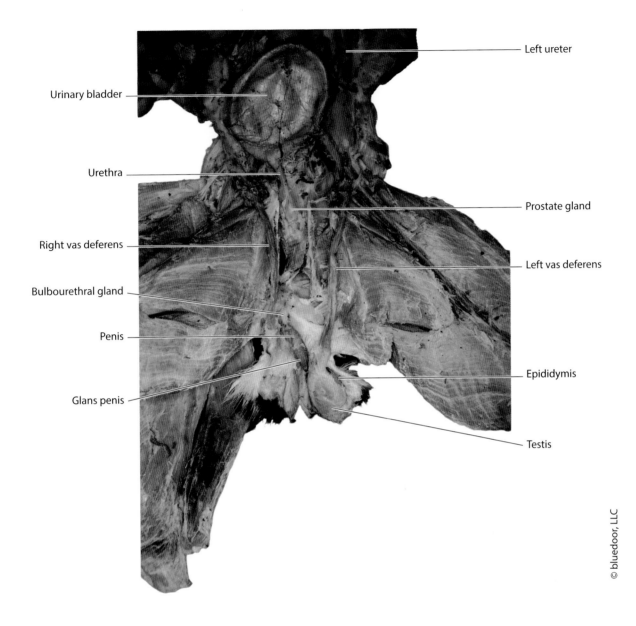

Left ureter

Urinary bladder

Urethra

Prostate gland

Right vas deferens

Left vas deferens

Bulbourethral gland

Penis

Glans penis

Epididymis

Testis

Figure 38: Male reproductive system, cat.